Natural Disasters

by Delana Heidrich

illustrated by Susan Kropa

cover by Jeff Van Kanegan

photo credit © Weatherstock

Publisher
Instructional Fair • TS Denison
Grand Rapids, Michigan 49544

ISBN: 1-56822-901-1
Natural Disasters
Copyright © 2000 by Instructional Fair Group
a Tribune Education Company
3195 Wilson Dr. NW
Grand Rapids, Michigan 49544

Table of Contents

Introduction

Hurricanes, earthquakes, floods, and volcanic eruptions are natural disasters. They destroy homes and businesses, knock out power and phone lines, collapse roads and bridges, devastate the natural habitats of wildlife, and kill multitudes of people, plants, and animals. They also produce fertile soils, thin out forests that have become too thick, and encourage philanthropy, heroism, and community cooperation.

Natural Disasters introduces students to the basic mechanisms of volcanoes, earthquakes, hurricanes, tornadoes, droughts, and floods and then highlights specific disasters and their effects on geography, geology, wildlife, and society. Students meet a high school drama class who survived a tornado that threw a bus onto their school's stage; experience the shake, rattle, and burning of San Francisco during its 1906 earthquake; and explore other fascinating stories about the forces of nature.

Each lesson presented in this book contains a single-page reading followed by theme-related activities that challenge students to interact with the lesson's material. Each lesson is self-contained and can be completed by students without teacher assistance. Some activities encourage students to write or draw, others to complete research, and others to think critically and problem solve.

Science and history teachers can use lessons from *Natural Disasters* to supplement textbook information about forces of nature or historical time periods, while English and language arts teachers can assign the lessons as high-interest reading comprehension projects. Assign the lessons individually or create extensive packets using each of the book's five natural divisions. Require students to complete the lessons as classwork, homework, or extra-credit projects; or allow them to be springboards to students' own research projects on the effects of natural disasters on humankind.

Volcanoes and Volcanic Eruptions

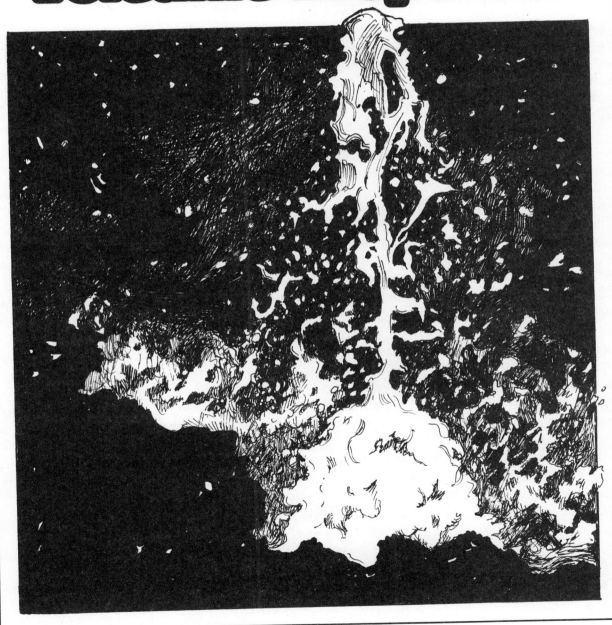

IF87013 Natural Disasters

What Is a Volcano?

To the untrained observer, a mountain is a mountain and an island is an island; but volcanologists know there is more to some land formations than meets the eye. A *volcano* is a vent or fissure in the earth's surface connected to an underground layer of molten rock and surrounded by such landforms as mountains and islands that have been created by erupted materials. Not all mountains, islands, and lakes are volcanoes, but some are. The Hawaiian islands are volcanoes. Washington's forest-covered Mt. Rainier, and Oregon's bowl-shaped Crater Lake are volcanoes.

How Do Volcanoes Form?

Volcanoes form due to interactions between the earth's two outer layers: the crust and the mantle. The earth's crust is like a cracked eggshell. It is comprised of 16 interconnected plates that "float" atop the mantle. Sometimes plates drift apart and offer pressurized magma located in the mantle a place to find release. Other times plates collide and one slips under the other. The *subducted* plate travels deep into the mantle where its rocks melt into magma and erupt again onto the earth's surface, creating cones or mountains of erupted materials.

Why Do Volcanoes Erupt?

When magma from the earth's mantle pushes through vents and fissures in the crust, a volcanic eruption occurs. Sometimes magma is thin and runny, allowing for the easy release of gases, so the eruption is nonexplosive; but sometimes magma is so thick and sticky that gases become trapped inside, causing a build-up of pressure that is released in a blast of magma and ash that shoots high into the sky.

Why Are Volcanic Eruptions Hazardous?

As *lava* (erupted magma) and *tephra* (the other particles that erupt from a volcano, including everything from ash to house-sized boulders) spew from a volcano, they create many dangerous side effects. Lava itself flows so slowly that a person can walk away from it, but when it mixes with water from streams, or melts snow and ice in its path, massive mudflows form that can bury whole communities at the rate of 60 miles per hour. Thick layers of ash and tephra can suffocate plants, animals, and humans and can affect both local and long-distance weather patterns. Additionally, coastline and underwater volcanoes can create enormous waves called *tsunamis* that can obliterate entire coastal communities.

Can Volcanic Eruptions Be Predicted?

Fertile volcanic ash and spectacular beauty draw tourists and residents to volcanic islands and mountains, so the ability to warn people about the possibility of an upcoming eruption is important. Volcanologists are able to make general predictions about the activities of volcanoes by monitoring slight rises in the level of magma inside a volcano's vent, small earthquakes that precede an eruption, increases in sulfur-dioxide emissions, physical swellings of mountain slopes, and changes in the temperature and chemistry of ground and spring waters. However, they cannot predict the exact date of eruption or level of explosiveness.

Effective precautions for residents of volcanic regions include utilizing farming methods that do not promote mudslides, keeping current on the activity volcanologists report from the area of the volcano, and heeding evacuation warnings when issued.

Volcanic Vocabulary

Scientists who study volcanoes have developed an extensive array of jargon to interpret the activity they study each day. Use encyclopedias, science textbooks, and reference books about volcanoes to help you define the volcanic vocabulary below in complete sentences. The first one has been done for you.

Volcanic Activity

1. Active Volcano: <u>An active volcano is one that is either currently erupting or has erupted in the recorded past and is expected to erupt again in the foreseeable future.</u>

2. Dormant Volcano: _____

_____

3. Extinct Volcano: _____

_____

Volcanic Materials

1. Tephra: _____
2. Pahoehoe: _____
3. Aa: _____
4. Lapilli: _____
5. Limuopele: _____
6. Pele's tears: _____
7. Nuée ardente: _____
8. Bombs: _____
9. Blocks: _____
10. Ash: _____

Eruption Styles

1. Strombolian: _____

_____

2. Vulcanian: _____

_____

3. Plinian: _____

_____

4. Hawaiian: _____

_____

Volcanic Rock

1. Basalt: _____
2. Dacite: _____
3. Rhyolite: _____
4. Andesite: _____
5. Ignimbrite: _____
6. Obsidian: _____
7. Pumice: _____

Classifying Volcanoes

Volcanoes can be classified according to form, structure, and level of activity. Study the following classifications of volcanoes and then answer the questions that follow.

Composite or Strato-Volcanoes are steep-sided symmetrical cones comprised of alternating layers of ash and lava. Commonly located near subducting tectonic plates, this type of volcano is highly explosive and frequently causes earthquakes, mudflows, landslides, and avalanches. Northern California's Mount Hood is a composite volcano.

Shield Volcanoes are large, gently sloped mountains comprised of layers of basalt rock that was very fluid lava at the time of eruption. Nonexplosive fountains define the eruptions of these volcanoes found in centrally located hotspots rather than near the edges of tectonic plates.

Submarine Volcanoes occur underwater where plates are pulled apart by convection, and lava is released into the earth's crust or along midocean ridges where plates have collided to create underwater volcanic mountain ranges.

Calderas have been nicknamed *inverse volcanoes* because they form huge craters when their highly explosive eruptions cause them to collapse on themselves. Yellowstone is a caldera complex.

Monogenetic Fields do not look like volcanoes because their hundreds or thousands of non-erupting vents and fissures are not concentrated in a single mountain or crater, but are spread out over a large surface area.

1. Which type of volcano produces midocean ridge basalt, the most common rock type found on earth?_____

2. San Francisco was built atop what kind of volcanic field? _____

3. Steep-sided Mount St. Helens is an example of which type of volcano? _____

4. An eruption from which type of volcano has never been witnessed first hand? _____

5. Which type of volcano which produces landslides, earthquakes, and explosive eruptions has caused more casualties than any other type?_____

6. Oregon's Crater Lake is an example of which type of volcano?_____

7. The nonexplosive, gently sloped Hawaiian islands exemplify which type of volcano?

   _____

8. Recent unrest has been detected at Yellowstone National Park and in Long Valley, California—two sites of which kind of volcano?_____

9. Which type of volcano collapses on itself, creating craters up to 15 miles in diameter?

   _____

10. Craters, or calderas, are sometimes found at the summits of which steep-sided volcanoes?

    _____

So You Want to Be a Volcanologist?

Men and women who study volcanoes advance science and influence human lives. Determine which of the following statements about becoming a volcanologist are true. Place in each blank a *T* for *true* or an *F* for *false*. The first one has been done for you.

__T__ 1. A person interested in a career as a volcanologist should complete as many high school math, science, and computer science classes as his/her high school offers.

_____ 2. The most important branch of science a volcanologist can study is biology.

_____ 3. Most volcanologists have a Ph.D. in geology.

_____ 4. Volcanologists' assistants and technicians, who seldom have a college degree, map volcanoes and analyze rock chemistry.

_____ 5. Most volcanologists work for the U.S. Geological Survey, a government agency.

_____ 6. The U.S. Geological Survey employs many volcanologists at their three observatories in Washington, Hawaii, and Alaska.

_____ 7. Alaska has 100 active volcanoes for volcanologists to monitor and study.

_____ 8. Most volcanologists teach volcanology courses at universities.

_____ 9. To become a volcanologist, one should major in volcanology in college.

_____ 10. Volcanologists work with city officials to warn people who live near active volcanoes when it is wise to evacuate their homes.

_____ 11. Physical volcanologists study the composition of volcanic products.

_____ 12. Geochemists study volcanic eruptions.

_____ 13. The job market is favorable for volcanologists today.

_____ 14. Most volcanologists gain valuable training experience through internship and advanced study projects as they prepare for graduate degrees.

_____ 15. College geology courses are broken down into many subdivisions including geomorphology, geochemistry, sedimentary geology, and petrology.

Valuable Volcanoes

Some earth changes caused by volcanic activity benefit mankind. Determine which type of benefit each result of volcanic activity listed below exemplifies. The first one has been done for you.

Benefit Categories

Energy Benefits   Commercial Benefits   Soil and Mineral Benefits

Soil and Mineral Benefits   1. The fertile soil produced by years of weathering and breakdown of volcanic rock made possible the development of early civilizations in the Mediterranean region.

_____   2. In some parts of the world, volcanic hot springs are used for doing laundry and warming greenhouses.

_____   3. Geothermal energy uses heat and steam from underground bodies of magma to provide residences and businesses with space heating and electricity.

_____   4. The beauty of many volcanic islands and mountains encourages tourism in many towns in volcanic regions.

_____   5. The fertile volcanic soil of the Hawaiian Islands produces sugar cane, pineapple, coffee beans, and macadamia nuts in abundance.

_____   6. Seventy percent of the homes in Iceland are heated using geothermal energy.

_____   7. Volcanic geysers, hot springs, and lakes provide many towns with tourist- and recreation-based economies.

_____   8. Iron, copper, zinc, nickel, silver, gold, and tin are all found in deposits underground where rising magma crystallized and hardened before reaching the earth's surface.

_____   9. Indonesia grows abundant supplies of rice in fertile soil enriched by the ash fallout of that country's active volcanoes.

_____ 10. Volcanic derivatives are used to produce road building materials, abrasive cleaning agents, and other chemical and industrial products.

Mount Vesuvius: Curtains for the City of Hercules

In southern Italy, near the shores of the Bay of Naples, stands Europe's only active volcano—Mount Vesuvius. The slopes of the deadly and dangerous mountain are covered with lush grasses, tall trees, and sprawling vineyards. A railroad track, beginning at the base, winds around the massive landform until it reaches the cinder cone's summit where an observatory sits close to the edge of a volcanic crater. Schools, churches, business districts, and private residences define communities all around the volcano. One million people live and work in the Vesuvius region. Thousands of others enjoy its cultural and recreational opportunities annually. Slumbering Mount Vesuvius is the picture of peace, but it sleeps indefinitely.

About 600 B.C. the cities of Pompeii and Herculaneum were founded at the foot of Mount Vesuvius. Developers could see that the caldera volcano had formed where an earlier strato-volcano had collapsed, but it was assumed that Vesuvius was by then extinct. Even in A.D. 63, when a major earthquake destroyed many pubic buildings in the two communities that had by then become Greek resort towns, the phenomenon was not thought to be related to volcanic activity. Then 16 years later, on August 24, in the year A.D. 79, the not-so-extinct Mount Vesuvius awakened with a start! A massive explosion blew off the top of the mountain and showered the city of Pompeii with 20 feet of hot ash and lava, and Herculaneum with 75 feet of mud. Although most of the inhabitants of the wealthy cities escaped, more than 2,000 did not.

The thick layer of wet ash and cinders that covered the eruption's victims and their towns created a hermetic seal. Although some residents of the Vesuvius cities returned to dig out their belongings shortly after the disaster, Herculaneum and Pompeii were soon abandoned and forgotten. The ancient cities of Italy remained buried for 1,500 years until workers on an underground water line rediscovered Pompeii. When they did, they found theaters, shops, homes, and the remains of people completely intact.

Mount Vesuvius has erupted about 50 times since that fateful day in A.D. 79, and some of the explosions have proven destructive. In 1631 mud and lava flows from the cinder cone's vent destroyed five towns and killed 3,000 people. In 1794 the volcano claimed the city of Terre del Greco. In 1906 ten continuous days of eruptions and mud flows claimed the lives of 2,000 area residents. The last major eruption occurred in 1944.

Today, no one pretends that Mount Vesuvius is extinct. Most activity seen on the volcano since the 1700s has been confined to the area within the crater at the mountain's summit, and nearly all volcanic behavior in the last 300 years has been noneruptive. Still, volcanologists monitor gas emissions, seismic readings, and physical changes on the mountain in hopes that area residents can receive warning from a few hours up to a few days should a large eruption ever threaten the region again. Geophysicists experiment with controlled explosions to determine the probable sequence of events should a major explosion occur. City officials and private citizens develop emergency plans of evacuation and economic recovery in the event of a disaster. Still, it has been predicted that a large eruption from the volcano today could destroy everything within a four-mile radius of the caldera within 15 minutes, threatening the lives and livelihoods of up to three million people.

Safety During Volcanic Eruptions

Would you choose to live in the shadow of an active or dormant volcano? _____ Why or why not? _____

_____

What risks do you knowingly take every day of your life? _____
Why do you take the risks? _____

_____

The American Red Cross has developed safety plans for those who reside in volcanic regions. Which of the following Red Cross instructions should be followed *before* a volcanic eruption, which should be followed *during* the event, and which should be followed *after* the eruption has ended? The first one has been identified for you. NOTE: Some precautions should be taken both during and after the eruption.

__During, After__ 1. When outside wear long sleeves and long pants, goggles, and a dust mask.

_____ 2. Follow the evacuation orders of city officials.

_____ 3. If caught indoors, close all windows and doors.

_____ 4. Learn about your community's warning system.

_____ 5. Plan an evacuation route for your family.

_____ 6. Exercising caution, clear roofs of heavy ashfall that can cause buildings to collapse.

_____ 7. Learn about common volcanic hazards including ash and mudflows, flash floods, landslides, rockfalls, earthquakes, ashfall and acid rain, and tsunamis.

_____ 8. If trapped outside, seek shelter indoors if possible. Move upslope from streams, and roll into a ball to protect your head during a rockfall.

_____ 9. Assist infants, the elderly, and people with disabilities.

_____ 10. Do not drive in heavy ashfall.

_____ 11. Avoid government restricted areas including river valleys and low-lying areas. Do not attempt to watch the erupting volcano close up.

_____ 12. Have on hand flashlights and batteries, a first-aid kit, emergency food and water, essential medicines, a nonelectric can opener, dust masks, and sturdy shoes.

_____ 13. Listen to a battery-operated radio for emergency updates.

Herculaneum, City of Hercules

According to legend, the city of Herculaneum, which was severely damaged by an earthquake in A.D. 63 and completely buried by the A.D. 79 eruption of Mount Vesuvius, was founded by the mythical Greek hero, Hercules. Read the brief summary of the fictional life of Hercules and then answer the questions about myths that follow.

The Life of Hercules: A Summary

According to legend, Hercules was the incredibly strong and courageous son of the god, Zeus, and a mortal woman, Alcmene. Because Zeus' goddess wife, Hera, was jealous of the illegitimate child, she caused him trouble all of his life. When Hercules was still an infant, Hera sent snakes to kill the child, but Hercules killed the snakes. When Hercules became a happy family man, Hera sent him into a rage in which he killed his own wife and children. As penance for his crime, Hercules was commanded to complete the challenging "Twelve Labors of Hercules":

1. Kill a lion which could not be injured by any weapon.
2. Kill a nine-headed monster who had one immortal head.
3. Capture a golden-horned stag that was sacred to the goddess of hunt.
4. Capture a great boar.
5. Clean up the stables of thousands of cattle.
6. Drive off a flock of man-eating birds.
7. Capture a mad bull.
8. Capture man-eating mares.
9. Present the girdle of the queen of the Amazons to the princess of Mycenae.
10. Capture the ox of a three-headed monster.
11. Gather golden apples.
12. Bring back a three-headed dog from the lower world.

After completing his tasks, Hercules remarried, but his wife was tricked into giving him a poisoned cloak that caused Hercules so much pain that he killed himself. After death, he married the goddess of youth and continued to be worshiped by the Greeks as both a god and a mortal hero.

1. Myths attempt to explain why things are the way they are. Some myths explain how the earth was created, how man learned about fire, or why humans are intelligent. What element of reality does the myth of Hercules attempt to explain?

   _____

   _____

2. While some scholars suggest mythological characters are completely fictitious, others believe they are exaggerated descriptions of real people. Does it seem the myth of Hercules is an exaggerated version of a true life, or a completely fictional story? Back up your answer with facts from the summary above.

   _____

   _____

3. Legends and tall tales are other types of folklore. On your own paper, compare and contrast myths with legends and tall tales.

Archeological Information

Systematic excavations of the cities of Pompeii and Herculaneum began in the mid-eighteenth century and continue today. Fine marble and bronze sculptures, floor and wall murals and mosaics, extensive paintings, libraries of papyrus rolls, theaters, temples, and shops have been found in the remains. From this evidence archeologists have hypothesized that both cities were resort areas for wealthy Romans. Make your own hypothesis about the lifestyles of the individuals or families whose homes are described below based on items that are located in their homes. Justify each hypothesis with specific items as has been done for you in the first problem.

1. DESCRIPTION: A red wagon and a swing set can be found in the front yard of the home. Inside, toys line the living room floor. Dark suits and business-style dresses hang in one of the bedroom closets. Two other bedrooms contain dressers with pants and shirts in children's sizes.

   Hypothesis: Two male children live at the home   Proof: toys, boys' clothes

   Hypothesis: A male and female adult live in the   Proof: male and female business-like
   home, both work   clothes

2. DESCRIPTION: Three college-level textbooks lie on a desk next to a stack of paper and a pencil in this single-room abode. A nearby garbage can is filled with soda cans and fast-food wrappers. Sweatpants, socks, and a football jersey are draped over the side of a twin-sized bed. A football helmet lies on the floor.

   Hypothesis: Proof:

   Hypothesis: Proof:

3. DESCRIPTION: A stack of diapers sits on a changing table inside a room decorated with Disney character wallpaper. The home's pantry is filled with fresh fruits, vegetables, spices, and jars of baby food. A refrigerator is filled with milk, eggs, margarine, and meats. Opened containers of sugar, flour, and baking soda sit on a kitchen counter.

   Hypothesis: Proof:

   Hypothesis: Proof:

4. DESCRIPTION: A garage beside the house contains both boxed and free-standing auto parts. The floor, walls, and counters in the garage are covered in oil. A jacked-up car sits in the middle of the building. A blue jumpsuit with a tag that indicates it is a "size small" hangs on a hook beside the door. In its pocket are a hair barrette and a diamond ring.

   Hypothesis: Proof:

   Hypothesis: Proof:

Auguste Ciparis: Condemned to Life in St. Pierre

The eruption at Mt. Vesuvius in A.D. 79 was not the only volcanic eruption in history to bury an entire population. On May 8, 1802, Mount Pelée, a volcano on the island of Martinique, covered the city of St. Pierre and all of its 29,000 inhabitants in ash and lava. That is because the governor of the town, Governor Mouttet, had convinced his constituency that there was nothing to be concerned about when the volcano began rumbling weeks earlier. Only the rich could afford to leave the island, and in the upcoming election only the rich were expected to vote for Mr. Mouttet. Clouds of ash and fumes dusted the city's streets and blew through open windows throughout the month of April. Small earthquakes shook the dishes inside kitchen cupboards several times throughout the month. Governor Mouttet convinced the local newspaper to downplay the dangers and even to contend that the opposing political party was creating public panic over nothing. On May 3, when a fissure explosion caused a severe mudflow, the governor hushed his constituency again. "The old woman is only grumbling again," he said, and he ordered the military to block all roads out of the city.

On May 5, a mudflow destroyed a sugar mill outside the city. On May 5 and 6, Mount Pelée sounded loud blasts. Then on May 8, 1802, at 7:52 a.m., she blew her top. A nuée ardente, or glowing avalanche, raced down the mountainside at 100 miles per hour. Large gassy clouds containing red-hot, broken rocks, each surrounded by a shell of gas—shot into the air, roared down the sides of the mountain, and buried Governor Mouttet and nearly every other person in the city that day.

Only two men survived the fierce eruption. One was a man who was on the outskirts of the city. Although severely burned, and forced to watch his family die in flames, Leon Compere-Leandre lived. Little is known about the posteruption years of Leon Compere-Leandre.

The other survivor was Auguste Ciparis, a condemned criminal who was also severely burned, even though protected by the thick-walled cell that was his home. What had Auguste heard and felt on that fateful day in 1802? Did he hear the rumblings and feel the quakes of the weeks past? Did he hear the rumors that the volcano could erupt? During the ultimate blast, did the ground rock beneath his feet? Did the roar of the volcanic eruption and the cries of its victims drift through his cell's single small window and into his ears? How did he come to be rescued? According to records, he waited three days and nights before he was rescued. What did he do and think inside his cell until the rescuers found him? Did he think he would ever be found? Did he think he would be put to death upon being rescued? (He was sentenced to be executed the morning of the eruption.) Round out the story of Auguste Ciparis by writing his account of May 8, 1902, and the days that followed in first person form on your own paper. Incidentally, Auguste Ciparis' sentence was commuted, and he went on to travel with the Barnum and Bailey Circus in a replica of his cell.

Krakatau: The Loudest Eruption in Recorded History

According to the Volcanic Explosivity Index, an 1883 eruption at Krakatau was not the most explosive volcanic eruption in recorded history. The 1815 eruption of Mount Tambora, its neighboring island, holds that distinction. Still, there was never a noise so loud as the one produced when a violent, volcanic explosion blew away two thirds of the island of Krakatau in the late nineteenth century.

Krakatau is a small island volcano located in southwestern Indonesia between Java and Sumatra. At one time, the island had an area of about 18 square miles, but today it claims a mere 6 square miles. That is because on August 27, 1883, a volcanic eruption collapsed most of the island 1,000 feet below sea level.

The "side effects" of the Krakatau explosion were unprecedented. The noise produced by the explosion was heard 3,000 miles away. The tsunami produced by an accompanying underwater earthquake reached 50 feet into the sky and traveled 8,000 miles. The eruption hurled 600-ton coral blocks from its central crater. Volcanic ash shot 30 miles into the sky and circled the globe for 13 days. Pumice produced by the eruption was seen floating across the Indian Ocean two years after the explosion. Observers around the world reported unusually bright sunrises and sunsets, hazy skies, "halloed" sun and moon sightings, and twilight effects for three years following the explosion. Although all residents of Krakatau had evacuated the island in anticipation of the explosion that was preceded by 100 days of lesser volcanic activity, the Krakatau eruption and tsunami obliterated 150 island villages along the coasts of the Sundra Strait. By the time the rumbling had ceased and the ash settled, over 36,000 people were dead.

Two months following the explosion, scientists arrived on the island. They collected and analyzed materials ejected from the mountain. Geologist R. M. Verbeck reported that his findings suggested sea water getting into the magma chamber under the volcano caused it to erupt. Today's geologists believe the massive explosion was rather caused by the displacement of dense dacitic magma by lighter basaltic magma—both of which were ejected from the mountain. Whatever the cause, the 1883 explosion was not the first nor the last volcanic eruption the little island would experience. Krakatau had erupted just three years prior to the big bang, and smaller eruptions have shaken the island a number of times since the 1883 explosion. In 1927 volcanic activity gave birth to a new island north of the Krakatau remains. Explosive eruptions haunt this new island as well. Today Krakatau and the new island are both active and uninhabitable.

Krakatau's Big, Bad Neighbor

Volcanologists take into account several factors in determining the size of a volcanic eruption. The Volcanic Explosivity Index considers type and frequency of volcanic activity, height of ash plume, volume of ashes, and other factors. Other indexes define the level of destructiveness of a volcano or its number of human victims. In terms of both deaths and explosivity, Tambora—also located on an Indonesian island—was the largest eruption in historical time. Use the facts about Tambora presented below to write a one-year anniversary news story about the eruption and its aftereffects.

Facts about the Tambora Eruption

1. Tambora is a stratovolcano located on the Sumbawa Island of Indonesia.
2. Tambora produced the largest eruption in recorded history in 1815.
3. The eruption column from Tambora reached 28 miles into the sky.
4. Lava and mudflows from the eruption were so violent they caused additional explosions.
5. Ten thousand people were killed by falling tephra and flowing lava and mud.
6. Because daily temperatures were abnormally low all over the Northern Hemisphere following the eruption, 1815 became known as the "Year Without a Summer."
7. Tambora's eruption ruined existing crops and caused weather that produced crop failures during the next year.
8. Eighty-two thousand people died of starvation due to the widespread famine caused by Tambora, resulting in a total of 92,000 deaths attributed to the disaster.

**Your One-Year Anniversary News Account
of the Tambora Eruption and Its Aftermath**

_____

_____

_____

_____

_____

_____

_____

_____

_____

_____

_____

_____

One Survivor's Story

Following the August 27, 1883, explosion at Krakatau, a survivor named Mrs. Beyerinck reported to an Indonesian newspaper the story of how the disaster affected her family. Learn the details of her account below and answer the questions that follow on your own paper.

In 1883 Mrs. Beyerinck, her husband, and their three children lived and worked on the island of Sumatra along with many other Dutch colonists. The family had established enough wealth to employ several servants and maintain two homes. Because Mr. Beyerinck was an officer of the colonial government, he and his wife were invited to formal parties, and his entire family was respected and happy. The only negative aspects of life on Sumatra were the frequent rumbling sounds and minor earth tremors that shook the ground beneath the feet of her inhabitants.

Beginning in the month of May, the earth tremors increased. In addition, light ash now fell from the sky on occasion and loud booms frightened Sumatra's residents. Fishermen reported that the ash and explosions originated on the neighboring island of Krakatau. Many residents were disbelieving since the long-quiet Krakatau was assumed to be extinct.

On Sunday, August 26, Mrs. Beyerinck was certain Krakatau was not extinct. Early in the day, she convinced her husband to leave an outdoor party when a loud explosion made her fear for the safety of her children at home. By nightfall, she convinced her husband to move the family to their second home near the middle of the island and away from the beach.

Soon after the Beyerincks and their servants entered the home and closed the doors and windows behind them just after midnight, smoldering ash and fiery pumice bombarded the island. Krakatau had blown her top. The Beyerincks' home collapsed around them. Its inhabitants were crushed and burned, but not killed. Mrs. Beyerinck's skin hung from her body in dirty ashen clumps and her legs were trapped under debris. Somehow she managed to free herself and run blindly out of her home, where she fell unconscious upon the ground.

When she recovered consciousness, Mrs. Beyerinck heard her husband calling her name. The ash-blackened sky and scattered debris made it challenging for Mrs. Beyerinck to make her way back to her home, but she managed. She discovered that her husband, children, and servants had all survived the fiery rain. Sadly, her 14-month-old son died shortly after being placed in her arms. The remaining family members and servants returned to the beach once the ash cleared from the sky enough for them to find their way. A day after the explosion, the Beyerincks were rescued from their devastated island home.

1. Why was the Krakatau explosion capable of surprising residents of neighboring islands?
2. How were the Beyerincks able to survive the explosion?
3. Sometimes age is called *the great equalizer* since it leaves its marks on rich, poor, white, black, religious, and nonreligious. How is a natural disaster a great equalizer?
4. What does the personal account of a disaster, such as the story of the Beyerinck family, offer a reader that a report of statistics and facts alone does not offer?

Avalanche!

One of the hazards of a volcanic explosion is that it can trigger avalanches of ice, rock, and snow to race from the mountain's cone to lands below. Snowmobiles, skiers, rifle shots, or even the flapping of a bird's wing can trigger avalanches too. Learn about the destructive forces of an avalanche as you fill in the blanks with numbers from the box below.

Number Box

1	20	⅓	5	100	50	110
	30	4	324	18,000	45	
	100,000	96	4,000	10		

1. Rescue workers find about _____% of avalanche victims alive.
2. Modern techniques including the use of radar, sonar, and lasers have been employed in locating avalanche victims, but dogs are still the most effective searchers. Dogs can search _____ square miles in less than _____ minutes, while it takes _____ people _____ hours to cover the same distance.
3. In 1910, when an avalanche in Washington state buried a passenger train, _____ people died.
4. As soon as avalanche victims are hit by powerful snow, ice, or rock, _____ of them die.
5. Survivors buried under the snows of an avalanche must be rescued within _____ hour(s) if they can be expected to survive.
6. A live avalanche victim rescued within a half an hour has a _____% chance of surviving.
7. From 1975 to 1986, _____ people died in avalanches in Switzerland.
8. In the western United States about _____ avalanches occur each year.
9. In 1962 an avalanche in Peru roared down a mountain for _____ miles, killing _____ people in its path.
10. An earthquake-triggered avalanche in the same country buried _____ people in rock, ice, and snow in a single 1970 avalanche.
11. An avalanche can rush down a mountain at _____ miles per hour or faster.
12. Slopes of 30 to _____ degrees are most susceptible to avalanches.

Crater Lake:
The Forming of a Caldera

Volcanologists are not the only scientists who study volcanoes, and active volcanoes are not the only volcanoes that get studied. Geologists who specialize in volcanic rock forms and who understand radioactive dating techniques describe volcanic activity that took place thousands of years ago. One such ancient eruption occurred at a place geologists call Mount Mazama.

Located in the southern part of the present-day state of Oregon, Mount Mazama does not look much like a mountain anymore. In fact, it looks like a lake. That's because 6,850 years ago, Mount Mazama blew its top off. Geologists estimate that a magma chamber under the volcanic complex had been building up pressure for somewhere between 15,000 and 40,000 years when the numerous shield and composite volcanoes that made up the mountain erupted violently, pouring lava into regions as far as 36 miles away, and blowing tephra 600 miles into what are now six U.S. states and two Canadian provinces.

The first eruption was probably followed by others, and the large volume of volcanic materials that erupted during the explosions soon drained the magma chamber beneath the landform and weakened the top of the mountain. Finally, the entire structure collapsed on itself producing what must have been a thundering sound as it formed a six-mile-wide, 1,932-foot-deep depression. Volcanic materials also produced 2,000-foot lava cliffs at the edge of the caldera and a "desert" of pumice rock north of its rim. In time, snow and rainfall filled the caldera, creating a lake, and further eruptions formed the cinder cone called Wizard Island.

Although the 200-foot deep pumice rock desert remains a barren land, the remaining Crater Lake region has recovered from the ancient explosion. Lichens and other simple plant types probably appeared around the lake first. As they began to decay and blow in the wind, they mixed with the ash of the volcano and created a rich soil. Grasses, ferns, and mosses probably took root next. Gradually, trees grew and animals returned to the Mount Mazama region. In 1888 William Gladstone Steel introduced 37 fingerling fish, which he had gathered from the Rogue River, into the lake. Today, there are thousands of fish in the deep lake itself and in the ponds of Wizard Island.

In 1902 the Crater Lake National Park was established. Today, Crater Lake is visited by half a million people annually. In addition to its magnificent beauty and awe-inspiring history, it offers a wide range of summer and winter recreational opportunities, including snowshoeing and cross-country skiing in the winter and hiking, picnicking, and camping in the summer. According to geologists, the volcano currently demonstrates no behavior that suggests another eruption of any size should occur in the foreseeable future. The volcano is considered extinct.

Understanding Lakes

Crater Lake is a unique body of water because it has no inlets and no outlets. The lake was formed and is maintained entirely from rainfall and snowmelt. How much do you know about inland bodies of water? Test your knowledge by filling in the following lake facts with words from the box below. The first one has been done for you.

Word Box

lack of precipitation	glaciers	glacier-margin lake	rivers
geological processes	one half	Lake Baikal	sulfates
5,371 feet	one fifth	industrial pollution	swamps
glacial-deposition	salt	carbonates	rainfall
evaporation	Caspian Sea	Lake Superior	springs

1. Some lakes are formed by _geological processes_ including the movement of large bodies of rock due to plate tectonics and the blocking of valleys by landslides, but most lake basins were carved out by _glaciers_.

2. Sources of a lake's water can include _____, _____, and _____.

3. Almost _____ of the earth's lakes can be found in Canada.

4. Lakes are not permanent features of the landscape. They disappear due to _____, _____, or a build up of sediment that turns them into _____.

5. Environmental problems that face lakes include _____ and poor agricultural practices.

6. A _____ is a temporary lake that forms at the margin of a glacier that forms a dam across a valley.

7. _____ lakes are formed from the sediment left after a glacier melts.

8. The largest lake in the United States is _____, which covers 31,700 square miles. The largest lake in the world, called the _____, covers 148,000 square miles.

9. _____, in Siberia, is the deepest lake in the world with _____ of water at its deepest place. As such, it contains _____ of all of the earth's fresh surface water.

10. The mineral content of lakes can include _____, _____, _____, and borates, or a combination of these substances.

Volcanic Legends and Myths

Ancient Romans believed the small island of Vulcano in the Mediterranean Sea was a chimney in the workshop of Vulcan, the blacksmith of the Roman gods. They believed smoke and ash had erupted from the "chimney" because Vulcan was making thunderbolts and weapons for the gods.

Old Hawaiian legends suggested that earthquakes and volcanic eruptions were caused by Pele, the goddess of volcanoes, when she became angry.

Even Crater Lake has its legend. Native Americans who lived near Mount Mazama before its collapse attributed its eruptions to a war between two gods, Llao and Skell.

Create your own volcanic myth. It does not need to include gods or goddesses, but you should create some workable characters and be certain your story explains the characteristics of volcanoes and their eruptions.

The Legend of the Great Volcano

_____

_____

_____

_____

_____

_____

_____

_____

_____

_____

_____

_____

_____

_____

_____

Name _____

Craters and Calderas

A *crater* is a depression at the top of a volcano that measures *less* than one mile across. A *caldera* is a depression at the top of a volcano that measures *more* than one mile across. Craters and calderas are sometimes the result of huge explosions that blow the tops right off volcanoes. More often they are created when so much magma is erupted from a volcano that the mountain can no longer support itself and so collapses. Many volcanoes contain craters or calderas similar to the one at Crater Lake. Use an atlas to help you determine where each of the crater- or caldera-type volcanoes below is located. Some locations will be used more than once.

Locations

Alaska, U.S.   New Zealand   Réunion Island   Italy
Mexico   Oregon, U.S.   Japan   Greece
Indonesia   France   Washington, U.S.   Hawaii, U.S.

_____ 1. Buldir Caldera

_____ 2. Taupo Caldera

_____ 3. Aso-san Volcano

_____ 4. Newberry Crater

_____ 5. Santorini Volcano

_____ 6. Piton de la Fournaise

_____ 7. Mount Vesuvius

_____ 8. Crater Lake

_____ 9. The Aleutian Islands calderas

_____ 10. Kawah Idjen Crater

_____ 11. Popocatépetl Volcano

_____ 12. Puys of Vache

_____ 13. Mauna Loa

_____ 14. Lassolas

_____ 15. Thíra

_____ 16. Krakatau

_____ 17. Mount St. Helens

Mount Saint Helens: Explosions, Landslides, and Ash

In 1975 geologists Dwight R. Crandell, Donald R. Mullineaux, and Meyer Rubin issued a report stating that their study of Mount Saint Helens suggested she might reawaken and erupt "perhaps before the end of the century." The 4.2 magnitude earthquake that shook the mountain five years later on March 20, 1980, added great weight to their prediction. Then on March 27, their forecast was confirmed when the long-dormant mountain began to spew ash and steam, creating a 6,000-foot smoke column and a 250-foot-wide crater within the existing summit depression.

For more than two months, Mount Saint Helens continued to blow steam and ash into the sky intermittently as the ground continued to shake with earthquakes, but the volcano released no lava. The magma instead began to swell on the north face of the mountain into what the anticipating geologists called the "bulge." Then on Sunday, May 18, 1980, at 8:32 a.m., an underground earthquake triggered the collapse of the "bulge" into the largest debris avalanche in recorded history. Volcanic materials and glacial ice raced downhill, covering 24 square miles and dumping enough debris into Spirit Lake to raise the water level 200 feet.

Within seconds of the onset of the avalanche, the pressured steam and magma below the surface unleashed a lateral blast of rock and ash that overtook the landslide, increasing its velocity from 220 miles an hour to 670 miles an hour. A vertical explosion followed the lateral blast shooting a mushroom-shaped ash cloud 12 miles into the sky, causing the mountain's summit crater to enlarge again. Meanwhile, magma flowed over the edges of the volcano's vent, rapidly losing gasses as it flowed into a fan-shaped zone of pumice north of the crater. Mudflows and floods followed these destructive forces.

By the time Mount Saint Helens quieted down again, 57 people, thousands of animals, and countless plants were destroyed in an area that covered 70 square miles. The mountain's elevation was decreased by 1,313 feet, and its top completely crumbled. Volcanic ash from the explosion traveled around the globe, depositing noticeable amounts in several northwestern states. Forestry losses caused by the disaster cost the federal, state, and private sectors a total of $450 million, and cleanup and property damage expenses added another $470 million in financial costs of the eruption.

Intermittent volcanic activity has shaken Mount Saint Helens since the huge 1980 eruption. Current monitoring and knowledge of the volcano's history suggests that another explosive eruption could occur before the mountain returns to a stable state. Yet already, the mountain has entered a natural recovery period which could last hundreds of years as rivers, streams, and forests "heal" and grow again. A national monument, which includes a visitor center, trails, campgrounds, and picnic areas, has been established in the area surrounding the volcano for visitors who wish to marvel at the incredible products of a volcano's activity. The Cascades Volcano Observatory has been built to allow scientists from around the world to study volcanic activity and its aftermath.

Mapping the Cascade Range

Mount Saint Helens is one of 15 volcanoes that are a part of the Cascade Range of the Pacific Northwest that stretches from Mount Garibaldi in British Columbia south to Lassen Peak in California. Refer to an atlas of North America to help you place the remaining 13 volcanoes of the Cascade Range on the map below.

Volcanic Peaks of the Cascade Range

Mount Baker	Crater Lake	Mount Rainier	Mount Shasta
Mount Jefferson	Mount Hood	Mount McLoughlin	Glacier Peak
Mount Adams	Three Sisters	Newberry Volcano	Medicine Lake
Mount St. Helens			

Mount Garibaldi

Lassen Peak

Volcanic Studies

The 1980 eruption at Mount Saint Helens in Washington has become the most extensively studied explosive eruption in history, but how do you study a volcano? At the United States' three observatories and one monitoring station, each located close to one or more active volcanoes, scientists strive to understand and monitor volcanic processes.

Determine whether the purpose of each of the following volcanic research techniques is to **A. Monitor and predict volcanic activity** or **B. Learn about a volcano's history.** The first one has been done for you.

__B__ 1. Radioactive carbon dating allows scientists to date organic materials located in different layers of volcanic rock to determine when eruptions occurred.

_____ 2. Tiltmeters allow scientists to measure changes in a volcano's slope due to the upward movement of underground magma.

_____ 3. By using laser light to measure the distance between two points, Electronic Distance Measurement (EDM) helps scientists estimate the depth and size of magma reservoirs.

_____ 4. Scientists map rock and ash layers to determine the extent of past volcanic activity.

_____ 5. Repeated surveying of volcanic mountains detects elevation changes that can forecast volcanic eruptions.

_____ 6. Scientists classify rock deposits to determine the dates and extent of past eruptions.

_____ 7. Distortions in the rings of trees located in volcanic regions convey the approximate date of trauma experienced by the organism.

_____ 8. Changes in the strength and magnitude of magnetic fields help scientists track the movement of underground magma.

_____ 9. Magnetic direction preserved in volcanic materials helps to date previous eruptions.

_____ 10. A system of satellites called Global Positioning System (GPS) measures changes in volcanoes before and during eruptions.

_____ 11. Seismographic equipment warns scientists of the frequency, magnitude, and location of earthquakes that are often precursors to volcanic eruptions.

_____ 12. Gas samples emitted from volcanoes are analyzed frequently for changes that indicate changes in the type, movement, or supply rate of a magma reservoir.

Twentieth-Century Eruptions

Mount Saint Helens is one of several volcanoes that erupted during the twentieth century. Match the following disasters with their descriptions by looking for geographical clues to help you.

_____ 1. This 1985 eruption triggered mudflows that killed 23,000 people when emergency measures in Armero, Colombia, proved to be inadequate.

_____ 2. Passengers were terrified when the jet aircraft they were riding temporarily lost all power as it entered the plume of this 1990 volcanic eruption in Alaska.

_____ 3. This 1912 eruption proved to be the largest United States eruption of the twentieth century.

_____ 4. Frequent eruptions of this Japanese volcano carry enough ash over the city of Kagoshima to create a visibility hazard to air transportation at the community's airport.

_____ 5. The violent eruption from this volcano killed 30,000 inhabitants of an island of the French West Indies in 1902.

_____ 6. This volcano was given its name meaning "Smoking Mountain" by the Aztec Indians who lived on and near it. It has erupted at least 36 times, with the latest cycle of activity beginning in 1996 and continuing into 1998.

_____ 7. Because ocean plates and earth plates meet here, three fourths of the earth's active and dormant volcanoes are located along this arc. Most of this century's volcanic eruptions—and seismic activity—have taken place in this region.

A. Redoubt Volcano, Alaska

B. Sakura-Jima, Japan

C. Mount Pelée, Martinique

D. Nevado del Ruiz, South America

E. Novarupta, Alaska

F. Popocatépetl, Mexico

G. Ring of Fire

Major Earthquakes

What Is an Earthquake?

An earthquake is the vibrating of the earth's crust caused by blocks of rock slipping against one another. Rock slippage may be the result of volcanic activity, human endeavors, or plate tectonics. Volcano-related earthquakes are usually low-magnitude events that warn volcanologists of impending eruptions and seldom cause large-scale destruction. Human-induced earthquakes are predictable, local tremors that occur with the filling of a new reservoir or the underground detonation of atomic explosives.

What Are Tectonic Earthquakes?

Tectonic earthquakes, caused by the crunching together, spreading apart, subduction, and collision of tectonic plates, account for nearly all of the destruction caused by earthquakes worldwide. As the plates slowly migrate under the continents and ocean floors, they accumulate great stresses which eventually exceed the strength of rocks along faults or fractures in the earth's crust. When this happens, rocks move suddenly around the fault and send seismic energy up, down, and out from the quake's focus.

Why Are Earthquakes Dangerous?

The rock movement around the fault during an earthquake seldom causes destruction since humans do not construct buildings or plan vacations directly atop visible crust fractions. Earthquakes are dangerous because seismic energy waves radiate up, down, and out from the quake's focus and cause buildings to collapse, power lines to go down, and landslides to occur. Additionally, quakes trigger tsunamis that threaten coastal regions and the liquefaction of loosely packed dense soils into virtual beds of quicksand that can swallow up trees, cars, and complete houses.

How Is the Intensity of Earthquakes Measured?

Assigning a quantity to the destruction caused by an earthquake is done using the Mercalli Scale which extends from 1 to 12, designating everything from tremors that can only be felt by people located on the second floor of buildings close to the quake's focal point, to shakes that collapse buildings and can be felt miles away. A more scientific approach to rating the intensity of earthquakes is to utilize the Richter Scale, which measures the energy released at the quake's focus. The Richter Scale runs from one to ten with each degree increasing tenfold. Therefore, a rating of 6 is 10 times more powerful than a rating of 5 and 100 times more powerful than one of 4.

Can Earthquakes Be Predicted?

Although earthquakes cannot be accurately predicted, scientists do monitor certain earth changes that can forecast the potential for danger. Some quakes are preceded by a lowering of area groundwater levels, detectable tilts and bulges in the earth's surface, and changes in the earth's magnetic field. Still earthquake prediction is a young science. The main focus of earthquake research is aimed at preventing death and destruction when the inevitable earth vibrations caused by the continual movement of tectonic plates occur.

Can the Negative Effects of Earthquakes Be Minimized?

Scientists study the sequence of foreshocks and aftershocks that precede and follow earthquakes. Such studies help them define the behavior of plate tectonics in specific locations so they can create seismic maps that inform earthquake zone residents of potential hazards near their homes and businesses. Engineers work with scientists to determine construction materials and procedures that are likely to stand up to ground vibrations when designing bridges, highways, and buildings in earthquake zones. City officials devise community-wide emergency plans that consider food, shelter, transportation, and medical needs in the event of a destructive quake. Private citizens who live in earthquake zones are encouraged to stock emergency supplies in their homes and decide with their family members on meeting places and emergency procedures in the event of a quake. All of these measures minimize the damage caused by the 15 or so major earthquakes that shake the planet annually.

Pinpointing Potential Problems

Some quakes occur in scattered areas around the globe, including underwater locations. However, 81% of the world's major earthquakes occur along the Circum-Pacific seismic belt around the edges of the Pacific Ocean. Another 17% occur along the Alpide Belt, which travels through the Himalayas and extends to the Mediterranean and out into the Atlantic Ocean.

Locate an earthquake distribution map in an encyclopedia, earth science textbook, or earthquake reference book to assist you in illustrating the Circum-Pacific Belt and Alpide Belt of seismic activity on the map below.

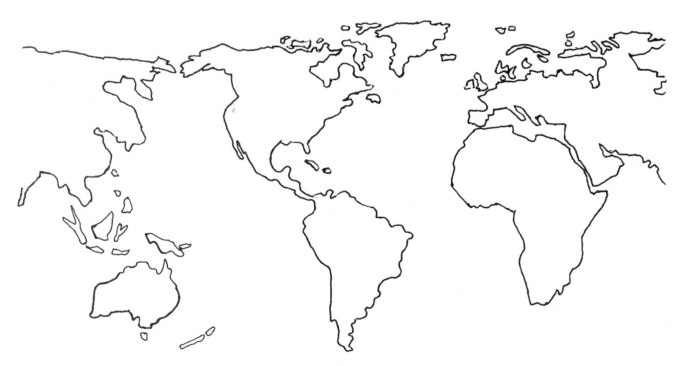

Studying the Earth's Vibrations

Mankind has been concerned about the nature of earthquakes since ancient times. Greek philosophers attributed earth vibrations to subterranean winds or fires inside the earth. Chang Heng, a Chinese scholar of the first century, constructed a circular bronze vessel lined with eight dragons. When earthquakes hit, one or more dragons would drop a ball from his mouth into the mouth of a frog below depending on the magnitude of the quake.

Match the following modern scientific devices used to monitor earthquakes with their descriptions below. The first one has been done for you.

__C__ 1. This instrument is inserted into a hole drilled into the ground and used to measure crustal deformation near an active fault.

_____ 2. This best-known seismic instrument records the earth's motions on a seismogram.

_____ 3. These instruments monitor changes in the level of an area's ground water table.

_____ 4. This system of satellites pinpoints the location of predetermined stations to assist in calculating earth movements caused by slipping.

_____ 5. One hundred twenty-five stations around the globe share findings of their seismic activity monitoring research through this worldwide network.

_____ 6. This process produces visual maps of the geology of a region including faults and subsurface gas-filled areas.

_____ 7. This instrument monitors changes in the distance between two piers located on opposite sides of a fault.

_____ 8. This instrument, which is installed along a fault line and powered by solar panels, measures changes in the magnetic field as often as every 10 minutes.

A. Seismic imaging

B. Fluid pressure transducers

C. Borehole strainmeter

D. Global Positioning System

E. Creepmeter

F. Magnetometer

G. Seismograph

H. World-Wide Standard Seismographic Network

Aftershocks and Body Waves

Use words from the word box and the clues provided to complete the crossword puzzle of earthquake terminology. There is no space between two-word answers in the puzzle.

Word Box

tsunami   seismologist   aftershock   body wave   crust   epicenter   hypocenter
plate   seismic   fault   focus   foreshock   liquefaction   magnitude   scale   intensity

ACROSS

8. scientist who studies earthquakes
9. The Richter _____ measures the magnitude of an earthquake.
11. the earth's outer layer
12. the point on the earth's surface directly above the hypocenter
14. a fracture in the earth's crust
15. A _____ boundary is where two or more tectonic plates meet.
16. point where the quake originated

DOWN

1. a wave that travels through the interior of the earth
2. soil acting like a liquid
3. calculated location of the focus
4. A _____ belt is also known as an earthquake zone.
5. a measure of energy released from an earthquake
6. measure of a quake's effects on humans and structures
7. small tremor that precedes larger quake
10. a minor vibration that follows a larger quake
13. a huge sea wave

San Francisco: 1906—Shake, Rattle, and Burn

At 5:12 a.m. on Wednesday, April 18, 1906, the slumbering residents of San Francisco, California, awoke with a start to 50 seconds of glass-shattering, roof-crumbling vibrations of the earth beneath their beds. The approximate 7.8-magnitude shocks that rattled their city were felt from southern Oregon to Los Angeles, and inland to the state of Nevada. San Francisco's City Hall—the largest civic building outside of Washington, D.C.,—was transformed into a pile of rubble in 20 seconds. Within minutes, the City by the Bay lay engulfed in blazing flames initiated by the overturning of stoves, breaking of chemical containers, and crossing of electrical wires. The principle water mains shattered, firefighters found themselves helpless to contain the devastating fire that blew with the wind from one wood-framed structure to the next down the hilly streets of San Francisco.

Thousands of mothers and fathers gathered their children and as many household items as they could load into baby wagons, wheelbarrows, and wooden trunks and escaped the flames by foot. Others took advantage of the free transportation offered by the president of the Southern Pacific Railroad and exited the city by train. Still others rode ferries north, across the bay. Those who found themselves trapped in the city endured three days and three nights of sweeping fires that were eventually contained only by the process of dynamiting structures downwind from the flames to deter the fire's advancement.

By 8:00 a.m. on the April 18, the city's police department had procured the help of the national guard and the navy in maintaining order, assisting the injured, and providing food, water, and shelter to residents who suddenly found themselves homeless. Makeshift hospitals and morgues were set up in fire stations, school buildings, and the police department's firing range. Operating automobiles were impressed to transport the sick, elderly, and injured to shelters or the ferry landing. Looters and burglars were captured and killed. Food was procured from grocery stores and offered to residents whose homes still stood and who had opened their doors to countless friends, neighbors, and strangers who needed a bed or a couch or a corner of floor to sleep on. Thousands of tents were erected in the city's parks, where the Los Angeles Relief Camp set up an outdoor kitchen that fed endless lines of refugees three times a day from great cooking pots of stew and potatoes. A bounty was offered for the thousands of rats that ran from the fires and threatened to be carriers of bubonic plague germs. Fully stocked ships that were scheduled to leave the bay stayed in the harbor, and train depots received 27,000 tons of supplies from neighboring cities and states.

In the end, San Francisco had incurred a loss of over 700 lives, 4.7 square miles of burned residential and business structures, and $275,000,000 in damages due entirely to the 5:12 a.m. quake of April 18 and the 26 aftershocks and city-sweeping fire that followed. The city was down, but far from out. One native who had escaped to Berkeley on April 18 returned ten days later to find the parks' bed sheet tents transformed into decent shelters constructed of window shutters and boat sails. City engineers were already procuring supplies to rebuild destroyed structures, and city merchants were offering four times the normal rent for structures that remained standing so they could get started rebuilding their businesses. Few survivors were determined to leave their hometown.

Fighting Fires

In 24 B.C. the Roman emperor Augustus established a group of fire-fighting "watchmen." In 1736 Ben Franklin organized the first permanent fire company in the United States. Research the history and methods employed in fire fighting to complete a report on the subject highlighting the following subheadings. You may use your own paper if you run out of space for your report on this page.

A History of Fire Fighting

_____
_____
_____
_____

Modern Fire Departments

_____
_____
_____
_____

Fire Prevention

_____
_____
_____
_____

Fighting Fires

_____
_____
_____
_____

Earthquakes in Review

Although incredible losses were suffered in San Francisco as a result of the 1906 quake, the subsequent systematic study of the event and its effects led to the modern theory of plate tectonics and the current use of safer building designs and materials in quake-prone cities. Decide which of the earthquake facts listed below are true findings from research conducted during and after the San Francisco earthquake and quakes around the world. The first one has been done for you.

__False__ 1. Clay is a good soil to build a home on in an earthquake zone.

_____ 2. Radioactive dating of plants found in soil layers disturbed by the 1906 quake in San Francisco suggest the last major quake to hit the Loma Prieta portion of the San Andreas fault occurred around A.D. 1600.

_____ 3. Historical records from Chinese and Japanese earthquakes dating back over a thousand years suggest giant earthquakes occur on large faults about once every 25 years.

_____ 4. It is believed that moderate earthquakes affected Northern California frequently for about 70 years before the 1906 major quake.

_____ 5. Historical findings suggest that short fault lines may generate frequent earthquakes, but they very seldom produce shocks of a magnitude of 7 or above.

_____ 6. Researching past earthquakes allows scientists to forecast the probability of further shocks, to create Seismic Zoning Maps that assign "danger levels" to various regions, and sometimes to predict the exact where and when of an area's next major quake.

_____ 7. It has been determined that the collapse of a portion of highway during a 1989 earthquake in Northern California can be attributed to that portion having been built on soft landfill material. This and similar findings have led scientists to the conclusion that liquefaction occurs more often on soft soils.

_____ 8. If a building is to withstand an earthquake, it is best to build it with strong beams and weak columns rather than weak beams and strong columns.

_____ 9. A building having short columns withstands an earthquake better than one with tall columns.

_____ 10. Reinforced concrete, framed walls filled in with cinder block or hollow brick, and steel construction materials all stand up well to earthquakes.

Chile: 1960—The Largest Earthquake on Record

The South American coastal nation of Chile is familiar with earth rumblings. That is because the Atacama Fault snakes through the mountainous terrain that runs the length of the country's west coast. From prehistory to modern times, the nation's people have been reminded that tectonic plates move and residents of their country best be ready for when they do. Still no one could have been prepared for the seismic activity that shook the region on a May morning in the mid-twentieth century.

The largest instrumentally recorded earthquake in history occurred off the coast of southern-central Chile on May 22, 1960. The shocks and waves created by the 9.5-magnitude underwater quake caused over one-half billion dollars in property damage, killed approximately 2,000 people, and rendered 2,000,000 survivors homeless.

The coastal Chilean towns of Valdivia and Puerto Montt were the first to be jolted when a foreshock rattled their communities 30 minutes prior to the main quake. Some of the towns' residents took to the streets while others tried to escape the shaking earth by sailing small ships into the Pacific Ocean. The people who stood in the streets were lucky. When the major earthquake crumbled their poorly constructed homes, the residents were not inside. The sailors were not so lucky. The submarine tremor triggered an 82-foot tsunami that rushed over 1,650 feet of coastland before returning to sea and fatally crashing atop all the boats in the bay.

The enormous wave then traveled thousands of miles in 14.8 hours until it reached the Hawaiian Islands, where it hit the city of Hilo with enough force and water to kill 61 people and wreak $24 million worth of damage. By the end of 22 hours, the tsunami had traveled 10,000 miles, where it killed 150 people on the coastline of Japan. Significant runup from the great wave was also reported on the shores of the Philippines and the continental United States as well.

In addition to the damage inflicted upon humans and human-made structures, the 1960 Chilean quake and tsunami altered natural landforms. Landslides changed the course of some rivers and dammed others to create new lakes. Ocean waters flooded thousands of Chilean acres, plowing over trees and drowning animals. And coastal lands downhill from the landslides turned into blocks of rock and mud and tumbled into the Pacific Ocean.

Although Chile is accustomed to frequent large-scale quakes, the 1960 disaster that hit that nation defines the dangers associated with shoreline earthquakes and resulting tsunamis.

Warning! Tsunami Approaching!

Although you may live thousands of miles away from the epicenter of an earthquake, you could be affected by the earth vibrations if you live in a coastal region and the distant quake generated a tsunami. The Pacific Tsunami Warning System, which includes most nations bordering the Pacific Ocean, conducts seismic and tidal research in an attempt to locate earthquakes, determines if a tsunami has been generated by the quake, and posts timely and effective warnings to minimize the deaths and destruction caused by these mammoth waves. Which of the following procedures should be followed in the event of a tsunami warning? Respond to each statement with a yes or a no.

_____ 1. When you hear an official tsunami warning for your area, get prepared to evacuate by changing into sturdy shoes and gathering necessary supplies. Continue to listen to radio or television emergency information to determine if evacuation will be necessary for your area.

_____ 2. If you are a science lover, and just must watch a tsunami hit shore, be certain you locate yourself on high ground since tsunamis can approach speeds of 500 miles per hour in the open ocean, causing "runup" on the shore as far as 90 feet, which is roughly the equivalent of an eight-story building.

_____ 3. If you have evacuated your home, you may return to assess damage as soon as the tsunami wave has hit shore and returned to sea.

After the tsunami threat has subsided, follow which of the following procedures:

_____ 1. Assist injured and trapped individuals and anyone else in need of special assistance.

_____ 2. Have an electrician check your wiring before using electricity in your home.

_____ 3. Allow mud inside your home to dry before shoveling for easier removal.

_____ 4. Throw out food that has come in contact with flood waters as it can be contaminated.

_____ 5. If water pipes are damaged, do not use tap water or flush toilets.

_____ 6. Leave doors and windows shut.

Just the Facts, Ma'am

On your own paper, organize the following facts into a question-and-answer informative brochure about tsunamis.

FACT ONE: Although tsunamis are ocean waves, they are misnamed when called "tidal waves" because they have nothing to do with the tides.

FACT TWO: A tsunami can be triggered by a volcanic eruption, a landslide, an earthquake, or the impact of an asteroid or comet.

FACT THREE: *Tsunami* is a Japanese word meaning "harbor wave."

FACT FOUR: The most deadly tsunami in recorded history occurred in response to the Krakatau volcanic eruption in 1883. Most of the 36,000 deaths can be attributed to the tsunami.

FACT FIVE: Most tsunamis are generated from undersea earthquakes, which occur frequently in subduction zones. When the quake hits, some of the seafloor moves upward, and some downward. Submarine landslides sometimes occur. The overlying water column rises and falls in an attempt to remain at an equilibrium and creates enormous ripples that spread outward at enormous speeds.

FACT SIX: A tsunami extends thousands of feet deep into the ocean.

FACT SEVEN: A tsunami can travel thousands of miles without losing much of its energy. Its speed is related to its depth, and can reach up to 500 miles per hour.

FACT EIGHT: A tsunami slows down as it reaches shore and therefore increases dramatically in height.

FACT NINE: The coastline and seafloor contours influence the height of a wave when it reaches shore. The average runup is 50 to 65 feet.

FACT TEN: Tsunamis do not all hit shore in the same way. Some appear as a wall of water, others as a single rising and falling tide, and others as a series of waves.

FACT ELEVEN: Using computer simulation to represent tsunamis helps scientists predict the height and inland reach of a tsunami hitting a given region and allows map-makers to create hazard maps that assist city officials in deciding about zoning matters, the placement of hospitals, and the effectiveness of evacuation routes.

Prince William Sound, Alaska: 1964—The Ruin of Fishing Communities

On March 27, 1964, at 5:36 p.m., an 8.4 magnitude earthquake, originating in Prince William Sound, Alaska, registered as the largest quake ever to hit a location within the borders of the United States. Sustaining a duration of nearly four minutes, it also earned the distinction of the longest lasting shock on record. The quake's intense and enduring vibrations triggered a tsunami with a maximum wave height of 2,211 feet that devastated coastal communities in Alaska, Hawaii, and California, caused minor damage in Texas, and was recorded on tide gauges in Cuba and Puerto Rico. All totaled, the quake, tsunami, and resulting landslides took the lives of 122 people, caused over $311 million in damages, and left thousands of Alaskans homeless and unemployed.

Most lives lost in the Prince William Sound earthquake occurred in small towns and villages along the shores of the sound. Chenega, a town of 80 people, lost 23 of its residents on that day. Thirteen of the 70 residents of Whittier were killed. Anchorage, Alaska's most populated city, on the other hand, lost only nine lives because the schools, stores, and offices that were destroyed were closed in recognition of Good Friday.

Property losses affected both the smaller communities surrounding Prince William Sound and Anchorage. Fishing fleets, harbor facilities, and canneries that kept the tiny Eskimo villages around the sound afloat financially were completely destroyed. In one village, every home was lost. In another, only the schoolhouse was left standing. In the town of Whittier two saw mills, one oil company, a railroad depot, and the harbor's boats and buildings were destroyed. In downtown Anchorage, the ground dropped 11 feet in places, damaging or destroying 30 blocks of homes and commercial buildings. The wealthy residents of the Turnagain Heights district watched their seacliff homes slide 700 feet into the bay. Water, gas, sewer, telephone, and electrical wires were inoperable throughout the region.

Natural landforms felt the quake, too. Mountains near the epicenter experienced nearly 2,000 avalanches as a result of the vibrations. Kodiak Island subsided six feet under the ocean floor. Southeast of Montague Island the ocean floor was uplifted 50 feet, and the beaches of the island itself found themselves to be 30 feet taller following the shock.

Still the Prince William Sound tale has a happy ending. What was learned from the scientific and sociological research that followed the quake has benefited earthquake-prone regions all over the world. President Johnson's declaration of the region as a disaster area set a precedent for federal funding of reconstruction following a massive earthquake. Studies of the region by the Geological Survey provided valuable information about how tectonic plates move and how structures can be constructed with that knowledge in mind. And the establishment of the Alaska Tsunami Warning Center that followed the 1964 disaster ensures that residents of the northern coastal towns of the Pacific Ocean will receive warning prior to the arrival of future tsunamis in their region.

Name _____

Turning Disaster into Delight

Arguably, every cloud has a silver lining; there is a light at the end of every tunnel. Although the Prince William Sound earthquake of 1964 was devastating for many villages in Alaska, the studies that were conducted following the disaster benefited future generations in preparing for earthquakes. What positive outcomes could follow the "disasters" described below?

1. In a weak moment, you joined other students in making fun of a handicapped boy who attends your school. Just as you are contributing your mean comments to your friends, the handicapped boy enters the room. How can you turn this disaster into delight?

_____

_____

2. While at the movies with a group of friends, your group becomes loud enough that the man in front of you asks you to quiet down. How can you turn this disaster into delight?

_____

_____

3. Because you watched the middle school football game yesterday afternoon instead of studying for your algebra test, you failed the exam. How can you turn this disaster into delight? _____

_____

4. This morning you got into a screaming match with your mother over something you later realized was really no big deal. How can you turn this disaster into delight?

_____

_____

5. While playing soccer in the living room with friends, you accidentally broke a window. How can you turn this disaster into delight? _____

_____

_____

6. When you enroll in a new middle school, you are informed that the school requires its students to take one semester of speech or drama. You are terrified of speaking or performing in front of people. How can you turn this disaster into delight? _____

_____

_____

7. You are an exceptional artist, but your small-town school does not offer art classes. How can you turn this disaster into delight? _____

_____

_____

Name _____

Measuring Quakes and Shakes

Two scales are used to measure the intensity of an earthquake. The Richter Scale, devised by Charles Francis Richter, mathematically determines the energy released at the quake's focus. The Richter Scale increases exponentially so that a 7 rating quake is 10 times as strong as a 6 rating quake, 100 times as strong as a 5 rating quake, 1,000 times stronger than a 4 rating quake, etc. The Mercalli Scale, devised by Giuseppe Mercalli, rates an earthquake in terms of observable criteria. Read the brief descriptions of each of the two scales below and then answer the questions that follow.

Mercalli's Scale

Value I: The quake is unfelt, but recorded on monitoring equipment.
Value II: The quake is felt by people at rest or on upper floors.
Value III: The quake is felt indoors. Hanging objects swing.
Value IV: Dishes rattle, and standing cars rock.
Value V: Liquids spill, doors swing, and sleepers awaken.
Value VI: Windows break, furniture moves, and walking becomes unsteady.
Value VII: Furniture breaks, large bells ring, and masonry cracks.
Value VIII: Tree branches break, houses move off foundations, and wet ground cracks.
Value IX: Underground pipes break, and people panic.
Value X: Masonry and frame structures are destroyed, large landslides occur, and rails bend.
Value XI: Ground cracks make highways impassable and render underground pipes out of service.
Value XII: Extensive damage occurs, objects are thrown into the air, and large rock masses are displaced.

The Richter Scale

Rating 2-3: The quake is unfelt, but recorded on monitoring equipment.
Rating 3-4: The quake is felt by many, but causes little damage.
Rating 4-5: The quake is felt by many and causes local damage.
Rating 5-6: The quake is destructive.
Rating 6-7: The quake causes major damage and destruction.
Rating 8-on: The quake is intense and destructive.
(Although the Richter scale has no upper limit, no quake of a magnitude beyond 9.5 has ever been recorded.)

1. Which scale is more scientific? _____
2. Which scale is more descriptive of the visible results of an earthquake? _____
3. What is the approximate Richter equivalent to a Mercalli Value I quake? _____
4. Which scale is dependent upon the location where observations are completed? _____
5. Which scale could rely in part upon the reports of people affected by the quake? _____
6. Which scale can be administered from miles away at an earthquake monitoring center? _____
7. Why might two scales exist? _____
8. Which scale would you refer to in devising building codes for a quake-prone region and why? _____

Rescue Missions

Although rescue workers use technologically advanced equipment and well-developed techniques to assist them in saving victims who have been trapped under buildings or debris following earthquakes, their job is complicated by many factors. Read the sentences below and decide whether each describes a rescuing technique or indicates a reason rescuing earthquake survivors is difficult. The first statement has been properly placed for you.

Rescuing Techniques	Rescuing Difficulties
__1__	_____
_____	_____
_____	_____
_____	_____
_____	
_____	

1. Helicopters assist rescuers in lifting earthquake survivors from wreckage.
2. Not all trapped survivors of earthquakes are conscious.
3. Rescuers need to be aware that an already damaged building could collapse more completely.
4. Thermal image cameras help locate live victims, detecting body heat through infrared radiation.
5. Damage to communication systems including phones and radios impairs the work of rescuers.
6. A trapped person's detector helps locate survivors by identifying vibrations.
7. A trapped person's detector includes a microphone and headphones that can be used by rescuers to communicate with live victims.
8. The difficulty in obtaining food and gas following an earthquake impairs the work of rescuers.
9. Spilled hazardous substances located in the debris of buildings under which live victims may be trapped can ignite into flames.
10. Dogs help locate earthquake victims.

New Madrid, Missouri: 1811–1812—Altering the Earth

Although 90% of all seismic energy takes place within the Pacific and Mediterranean Belt Area where plates meet and sometimes collide, the tremors that caused the most extensive physiographic changes in the United States were a series of midplate earthquakes that occurred in the region where the Mississippi and Ohio Rivers meet, perhaps because the earth's crust attempts to tear apart at that location. The so-called New Madrid, Missouri, quakes took place from December 1811 through March 1812. The series included 200 moderate to severe quakes, including several that exceeded a magnitude of 8, and nearly 2,000 minor tremors that originated in Arkansas and Missouri and were felt in the states of Ohio, Missouri, Illinois, Indiana, Arkansas, Kentucky, Tennessee, Virginia, Washington, D.C., and the Carolinas. The four most devastating shocks, which were felt as far as 1,000 miles from their epicenters, changed the face of the Mississippi River Valley forever.

Still few lives were lost and little property was damaged by the massive quakes. That is because only about 3,000 trappers and farmers resided in sturdy log cabin communities in the region during the early 1800s. The most violent quake on February 7, 1812, startled the trappers and farmers out of their beds that morning and tossed boats along the Mississippi as though they were adrift in a sea and not a river. Yet, the greatest effect of the quake was not suffered by the people, but by the land.

The New Madrid quakes cracked the ground, bent trees, triggered landslides, and rerouted the Mississippi River. During one of the shocks, the naturalist and artist John Audubon, who was riding horseback in Kentucky, compared the appearance of the landscape surrounding him to the "ruffled waters of a lake." Forests flooded, lakes formed, the earth rose in some regions and sank in others, islands of the Mississippi River disappeared, and the river's banks crumbled into the water. Whole forests crashed to the ground, giant fissures cracked open the earth's crust, and strange geysers of sand shot into the air. The most severe shocks caused clocks to stop in Boston, windows to rattle in Washington D.C., and plaster to crack in Virginia and North and South Carolina.

Today, the Mississippi River Valley is seismically calm, allowing residents and visitors to forget the past, but the threat of vibrations caused by the movement of the earth's crust remains strong in the United States midplate region. The next time a quake hits the region, it will not startle a few trappers our of their beds. It will threaten over 12 million—perhaps unexpecting—people who work and reside from Little Rock, Arkansas, to Evansville, Indiana.

Name _____

Mapping Disaster

The 1811-1812 series of earthquakes known as the New Madrid quakes were felt as far as 1,000 miles away from their source. Study the effects of the shocks on the Mississippi River states by looking at the map below and answering the questions that follow. You may need to refer to an atlas to answer some questions.

1. The first two quakes of the 1811-1812 series occurred in northeastern Arkansas. What letter on the map signifies northeastern Arkansas? _____

2. New Madrid was the epicenter of the most severe quakes. In what state is New Madrid located? _____

3. The course of the Mississippi River was affected by the 1811-1812 quakes. Only a portion of the Mississippi River can be seen on this map. Do you know where the river begins and ends? _____

4. The New Madrid quakes affected the region where the Ohio River flows into the Mississippi River around Cairo, Illinois. Where does the Ohio River originate (not shown on map)? _____

5. Sunken lands, fissures, and landslides triggered by the 1811-1812 quakes affected an area that stretched from the eastern border of Tennessee to the western border and from Cairo, Illinois, in the north to Memphis, Tennessee, to the south. Which letters on the map symbolize Memphis and Cairo? _____

6. One of the New Madrid quakes caused property damage as far away as Cincinnati, Ohio. Which letter on the map shows the location of Cincinnati? _____

7. Lake St. Francis was formed by subsidence resulting from the 1811-1812 series of quakes. In what state is Lake St. Francis located? _____

8. St. Louis experienced a great deal of damage during the fourth of the 1811-1812 major quakes. In what state is St. Louis located? _____

John James Audubon

John Audubon was one of the men who wrote about the New Madrid quakes. Learn about the life of Mr. Audubon as you match the introductory sentences with the paragraphs they should begin.

Introductory Sentences Box

- During his lifetime, John James Audubon lived in Haiti, France, England, and the United States.
- John Audubon studied and drew pictures of American birds.
- The work of John Audubon continued to be appreciated after his death in 1851.
- The Scottish naturalist William MacGillivray was instrumental in transforming *The Birds of America* into more than just a picture book.

1. _____

A book he had begun with his sons and the naturalist John Bachman 13 years prior was published in 1845 under the title *The Viviparous Quadrupeds of North America.* His hand-colored, realistic portrayals of American birds continues to be recognized by naturalists and the general public as the definitive visual study of this country's bird species. The National Audubon Society was founded in his honor.

2. _____

Born in Haiti to a French naval officer and his wife, he was educated in France. As a young man, he moved to Philadelphia, and then to Louisville, Kentucky, and on to Henderson, Kentucky. Later he moved to England to seek a publisher for his drawings of North American birds. Audubon died on a rural estate in New York.

3. _____

Although he operated a general store when he lived in Kentucky, it was not very successful, and by the time he reached the age of 35, Audubon decided to dedicate all of his time to his artwork. His work was well-received in Europe, where it led to exhibitions and the publication of his masterpiece, *The Birds of America.* In his lifetime, Audubon depicted in realistic drawings thousands of birds of North America.

4. _____

When he saw the 435 hand-colored plates Audubon had produced depicting 1,065 birds, he wrote a companion volume describing the habits and characteristics of the bird species portrayed. Eventually, the two books were combined into a seven-volume study of both the physical appearance and behavioral habits of North American birds.

Great Earthquakes Worldwide

Match the following earthquakes from history with their descriptions by locating them in encyclopedias, reference books about earthquakes, or on Internet sites about the location of each quake or earthquakes in general. The first one has been done for you.

__C__ 1. This 1988 earthquake left 400,000 people homeless when 58 towns and villages were completely destroyed.

_____ 2. This most devastating earthquake in recorded history killed 830,000 people in 1556.

_____ 3. This quake that hit China in 1976 killed 242,000 people.

_____ 4. The 10,000 deaths and massive destruction that resulted from this quake can be attributed not only to shaking in the region of the epicenter, but also to the widespread fires and a massive tsunami that was noticed as far away as England.

_____ 5. The narrow streets in the city affected by this quake and the poorly constructed buildings of river pebbles and bricks contributed to the quake's death toll of 50,000.

_____ 6. This Japanese quake crashed buildings to the ground and triggered an uncontrollable fire that burned people alive and a tsunami that measured 36 feet at the shore, killing 140,000 in all.

_____ 7. Although only 61 lives were lost in this recent quake on United States soil, 40,000 buildings were damaged and 20,000 people left homeless.

_____ 8. Landslides were primarily responsible for the 50,000 deaths caused by this 1990 Mideastern earthquake.

A. Tangshan, China
   July 28, 1976

B. Tokyo-Yokohama, Japan
   September 1, 1923

C. Armenia
   December 7, 1988

D. Iran
   June 21, 1990

E. Shensi, China
   January 24, 1556

F. Lisbon, Portugal
   November 1, 1755

G. Messina, Sicily, Italy
   December 28, 1908

H. Northridge, California
   January 17, 1994

Hurricanes and Tornadoes

Hurricanes and Tornadoes: What's the Difference?

What Is a Hurricane?

A *hurricane* is a huge mass of wind and water circling around a low-pressure center at speeds of 74 to 155 miles per hour. A hurricane can develop in the Atlantic Ocean, the Caribbean Sea, or the Gulf of Mexico during the months of August, September, or October when warm air near the surface of the ocean picks up water and rises. Cooler air takes the place of the risen air and ascends after it too has warmed and picked up water. The process continues until the large column of rising air, powered by the condensing of its water vapors into droplets, begins to blow counterclockwise around the low-pressure "eye" of the storm at speeds exceeding 74 miles per hour.

Why Is a Hurricane Dangerous?

The destruction caused by a hurricane that reaches land is a result of the storm's high winds that can uproot trees and smash concrete structures. It can also create enormous waves of the storm's "surge" that can flood up to 100 miles of coastline in 10 feet of water. The storm's heavy rains can dump 10 inches of water on regions hundreds of miles inland from where the storm originally makes landfall.

Can a Hurricane Be Predicted?

Unlike the shaking of a high magnitude earthquake or the explosion of an erupting volcano, the winds and rains of a hurricane can be quite accurately predicted. An average of 65 tropical storms that develop in the oceans, seas, and gulfs around the world become hurricanes, or *typhoons*, as they are called in the western Pacific. Meteorologists follow the development of each storm with the use of satellite pictures of the developing *cyclone*—the generic name for any violently rotating windstorm. They also study reports from scientists who fly airplanes directly into the storm while it is still at sea to measure air temperatures, air pressure, and water content. Hurricane experts at the National Hurricane Center combine the findings from satellite images and reports from the scientists who fly hurricane reconnaissance planes with instrument readings from weather balloons and computer models of advancing storms to predict the movement of a cyclone. With our current level of knowledge and technology, meteorologists are able to alert people to the dangers of an approaching hurricane days before it hits the land.

What Is a Tornado?

A *tornado* is a whirling column of wind that spins counterclockwise and extends from a cloud to the surface of the earth. It is visible because of the dust it sucks up and the water vapors that condense into droplets in the funnel's center. The exact cause of a tornado is not yet understood, but it is always associated with atmospheric instability most often in the form of a thunderstorm. Scientists also know that a tornado is most likely to occur in temperate latitudes during the spring in the United States.

A tornado can last from a few seconds to a few hours, be a few yards to a half a mile wide, travel from a few yards to a couple hundred miles, create winds from 50 m.p.h. to 300 m.p.h., and contain from one to several vortexes or "funnels."

Why Is a Tornado Dangerous?

Although a tornado does not last as long as a hurricane or affect nearly as large a region, it can be extremely destructive. The strong, concentrated winds of a tornado can break windows, uproot trees, and rip roofs right off the tops of buildings. The glass, boards, branches, trees, and other flying debris propelled through the air when a tornado hits can pierce trees, houses, or hapless victims. The vortex of a tornado can lift everything from automobiles to mobile homes right off the ground. And because the path of a tornado is not predictable—sometimes sweeping across a few miles and other times hopping about from town to town over a couple hundred mile stretch—victims have little time to prepare for the destruction one might bring.

Can a Tornado Be Predicted?

Although scientists do not yet fully understand the mechanisms of a tornado or the path it chooses, they have come to recognize the conditions that precede a twister's development. Tornado researchers analyze meteorological findings and Doppler radar readings around thunderstorms and chase storms with a Totable Tornado Observatory that contains instruments which measure what is going on in and around a striking tornado.

By monitoring weather conditions, meteorologists are able to issue tornado watches when conditions are ripe for the creation of a twister. Still the formation of a tornado is so unpredictable that when a warning is issued indicating that an actual tornado has been sighted, residents in the path of the storm may only have minutes to run to a basement or seek cover in a ditch along the road.

How Does a Hurricane Differ from a Tornado?

A hurricane and a tornado are each a form of a cyclone, or a low atmospheric pressure region (the storm's eye) surrounded by a counterclockwise rotating wind system, but the characteristics of each differ greatly.

A hurricane is like an enormous machine that keeps the planet's temperature in balance by moving excess hot air from the tropics into the middle latitudes. By studying tropical storms and general weather patterns, meteorologists have developed enough of an understanding of hurricanes to predict their formation, duration, and path.

A tornado is like a concentrated hurricane that forms over the land for reasons scientists do not understand nearly as well. Its winds, which can reach speeds twice that of a hurricane's winds, come and go quickly, affecting a relatively small region, with little warning and seemingly little meteorological reason. Because of our limited understanding of tornadoes, their formation, duration, and path cannot be as accurately predicted as that of hurricanes.

Tornado Terms and Hurricane Words

Read the definitions of the following hurricane and tornado terms and then choose five terms to include in a story you write on your own paper about a tornado or hurricane.

Tornado Terms

Unstable Atmosphere—A condition in which displaced air becomes less dense as it rises and therefore continues to rise and sometimes forms cumulus clouds or thunderstorms—the precursor of tornadoes.

Supercell—A severe thunderstorm that is the "mother" of hail, straight-line winds, and nearly all violent tornadoes.

Tornado Alley—The name given to a geographical region that stretches from Texas north to Nebraska and Iowa where most United States' tornadoes occur.

Updraft—A current of air that rises. If an updraft contains enough moisture, it can form cumulus clouds or thunderstorms.

Downdraft—The sudden descent of cool air to the ground, usually along with rain in the form of a shower or thunderstorm.

Doppler Radar—Weather radar, which measures the speed and direction of wind and rain.

TOTO—A Totable Tornado Observatory is placed on the front of a car which "chases" tornadoes in an attempt to measure the speed, direction, and temperature of wind inside a tornado as well as atmospheric pressure and electric field strength.

Hurricane Words

Eye—The term that refers to the 5- to 60-mile-wide calm, rain-free center of a hurricane.

Eye Wall—A band of cumulonimbus clouds, intense rainfall, and strong winds that surrounds the eye of a hurricane.

Landfall—The point at which the eye of a hurricane first reaches a mass of land.

Storm Surge—The increase in the height of waves, caused by a hurricane. A storm surge can increase a wave's height by as much as 24 feet, and can scour away sand and carry away boats, buildings, and debris.

Reconnaissance Aircraft—Weather planes that are equipped with scientific instrumentation that fly directly into a hurricane that is still at sea.

Doldrums—An ocean region near the equator that is calm itself but can give birth to tropical storms because of the warm temperatures of its water and low pressure zones.

Tropical Depression—Thunderstorms over the ocean that organize into a swirl.

Tropical Storm—A tropical depression that has obtained wind speeds exceeding 39 miles per hour.

Rain Bands—The 3- to 30-mile-wide bands of thunderstorms that spiral around the eye to form a hurricane.

I Didn't Know That!

How much do you know about hurricanes and tornadoes? Use an encyclopedia, science text, or weather resource book from your school's library to help you determine which of the following statements are true. The first one has been done for you.

__T__ 1. The average lifetime of a hurricane is ten days while the average lifetime of a tornado is several hours.

_____ 2. The low pressure area at the center of a tornado can cause unventilated buildings to explode.

_____ 3. In a single day, a hurricane can produce the amount of energy equal to supply the nation's electrical needs for six months.

_____ 4. Tornadoes cause more deaths in the United States annually than any other natural phenomenon.

_____ 5. Tornadoes sneak up on unexpecting victims because they are so quiet.

_____ 6. In addition to the storm that hits land, hurricanes also create under-ocean currents that rock the sea well below the surface.

_____ 7. Although there is no "tornado season," tornadoes most commonly occur in the months of October, November, and December.

_____ 8. Low-level moisture, atmospheric instability, and a "trigger" such as the arrival of a cold front are required for the development of thunderstorms and tornadoes.

_____ 9. As the eye of a hurricane grows, the resulting storm intensifies.

_____ 10. In the past 100 years, the number of U.S. deaths attributed to hurricanes has decreased while the cost of hurricane damage has increased.

_____ 11. Hurricanes and tornadoes both develop out of thunderstorms.

_____ 12. For a hurricane to form above an ocean, the water's temperatures must be less than 80 degrees Fahrenheit.

_____ 13. A tornado can take several forms including a funnel shape, a rope-like shape, a multiple-vortex form, and the mesocyclones of supercell thunderstorms.

_____ 14. When thunderstorms that form over an ocean organize into a swirl, they are called tropical storms.

_____ 15. A hurricane weakens once it reaches land.

_____ 16. Air in the eye of a hurricane is calm so when a storm hits a community, its members endure a storm of several hours, a calm period, and then a whole new storm that blows in the opposite direction of the first.

_____ 17. A supercell thunderstorm can travel 300 miles and spawn one tornado after another along with producing heavy rainfall and hail.

_____ 18. Much damage historically attributed to tornadoes may have really been caused by the recently discovered "downbursts—" downdrafts produced by thunderstorms that actually touch ground.

_____ 19. A tornado can be 300–400 miles in diameter whereas a hurricane is seldom as wide as 1 mile across.

_____ 20. Doppler radar helps forecast tornadoes by displaying the swirling winds that sometimes precede their formation.

Thunderstorms Gone Mad

The Saffir-Simpson Damage-Potential Scale measures the damage caused by a hurricane. The Fujita Wind Damage Scale measures the damage caused by a tornado. Compare the two scales and then match the descriptions below each with their appropriate classification. The first one has been done for you.

The Fujita Wind Damage Scale

Classification	Wind Speeds	Damage Level	Matching Description
F0	40–72 m.p.h.	Light	A
F1	73–112 m.p.h.	Moderate	_____
F2	113–157 m.p.h.	Severe	_____
F3	158–206 m.p.h.	Considerable	_____
F4	207–260 m.p.h.	Devastating	_____
F5	261–318 m.p.h.	Incredible	_____

A. Tree branches and TV antennas break. Road signs and chimneys are damaged.
B. Large missiles of debris generated. Frame homes leveled. Resting cars picked up and moved.
C. Mobile homes overturned. Moving cars pushed off road. Small trees uprooted.
D. Trains overturned. Large trees flattened or uprooted. Roofs torn off.
E. Slab houses leveled. Frame houses carried a distance. Reinforced concrete structures severely damaged. Auto-sized missiles propelled over 100 yards.
F. Light object missiles generated. Boxcars pushed over. Roofs blown off houses.

The Saffir-Simpson Damage-Potential Scale

Category	Wind Speeds	Storm Surge (in feet)	Damage Level	Matching Description
1	74-95 m.p.h.	4–5	Minimal	_____
2	96-110 m.p.h.	6–8	Moderate	_____
3	111-130 m.p.h.	9–12	Extensive	_____
4	131-155 m.p.h.	13–18	Extreme	_____
5	155+ m.p.h.	18+	Catastrophic	_____

A. Damage to street signs, windows, roofing materials, and trees. Coastal roads cut off. Shoreline residents evacuated.
B. Buildings overturned, blown away, or destroyed. Major erosion of beaches. Residents evacuated within 10 miles of shore.
C. Mobile homes destroyed. Serious flooding along coast. Residents several blocks from shore evacuated.
D. Damage primarily restricted to trees and shrubbery. No evacuation requirements.
E. Extensive damage to roofs, windows, and doors. Land 10 feet above sea level flooded. Residents within 500 yards from shore evacuated.

The Great Galveston Gale of 1900: Island Disaster!

Just off the Texas coast, in the Gulf of Mexico, lies a barrier island called Galveston. Galveston Island is a long, narrow strip of land, no wider than three miles across at its widest, and averaging just 4.5 feet above sea level in elevation. In 1900 the Texas town had a population of 38,000 people. Its wharves served 1,000 trading ships a year, and its single bridge and countless ports welcomed to its shores thousands of tourists annually. Wealthy Galveston was considered the "New York City of Texas."

If satellite images would have been available at the turn on the century to forewarn Galveston's residents and visitors of an approaching Category 4 hurricane, they would likely have evacuated their homes and left their island paradise before dawn on Saturday, September 8, 1900. As it was, local meteorologist Dr. Isaac Cline had little more to rely on than his own intuition in predicting the magnitude of a storm that the National Weather Bureau had telegraphed was coming his way. Although weather conditions were calm on the morning of September 7, Dr. Cline predicted that the rapidly lowering barometric readings and rough seas he witnessed might signal trouble. He telegraphed Washington, D.C., to inform the nation's capital that much of Galveston might soon be underwater. Alarmed by the winds and tides on the morning of September 8, Dr. Cline steered a horse-drawn buggy up and down the beaches of his island home to warn residents to seek shelter further inland. Four hundred refugees flooded Galveston's Sacred Heart Church. Fifty men, women, and children huddled in Dr. Cline's own home.

Around 4:00 p.m. tide surges from both north and south of the island hit the shore, destroying every building within three blocks of the beach. The bridge to mainland Texas was covered in water. Winds of 84 m.p.h. slammed into trees, buildings, and animals. Another surge hit the shore, this time creating a 20-foot-high wave. Winds up to 120 m.p.h. now ripped the city apart. Wood and brick buildings alike toppled into the sea. Helpless victims were swept along with them. Ninety children were killed when the Catholic orphanage was struck by waves and winds. Thirty-two of the people who took refuge in Dr. Cline's home, including his wife, were swept to sea. Dr. Cline and the other survivors drifted helplessly atop debris, protecting themselves "from the flying timber by holding planks between [themselves] and the wind."

When the hurricane finally passed, weakening into a tropical storm as it tracked up through Oklahoma and Kansas, survivors of the Galveston gale were faced with the remains of 36,000 houses and the bodies of 7,200 dead friends and neighbors. Proud single dwellings were piled into huge heaps of broken glass and splintered wood. Telephone poles arched to the ground. Animal carcasses lay beside human remains.

The elements had struck. The survivors of the Galveston gale struck back. Within six days, the island's residents had built a bridge to the mainland. Within a few months, buildings that had survived the storm were jacked up and sandfill was used to raise them seven or eight feet. In 1902 work began on the construction of a 3-mile long, 17-feet-high, 15-feet-wide reinforced concrete wall as a shield against the next storm. In 1904 the wall was completed. In 1915 another Category 4 hurricane hit. This time, Galveston Island sustained little damage.

Barrier Islands from Texas to Maine

Galveston and the other 295 barrier islands that line the coast from Texas to Maine often take the first blows from incoming hurricanes. Their residents must be especially prepared to evacuate their homes and island in case of hurricane warnings since their evacuation routes require the use of bridges and ferries that can become overcrowded if all wait until the last hours. Off the coast of which state is each of the following islands located? Complete an Internet search or use an atlas to help you find out.

1. Marsh Island is off the coast of _____.
2. Ossabaw Island is off the coast of _____.
3. San Jose Island is off the coast of _____.
4. Horn Island is off the coast of _____.
5. Dauphin Island is off the coast of _____.
6. Hilton Head Island is off the coast of _____.
7. Breton Island is off the coast of _____.
8. Block Island is off the coast of _____.
9. Cross Island is off the coast of _____.
10. Martha's Vineyard is off the coast of _____.
11. Fisher's Island is off the coast of _____.
12. Mount Desert Island is off the coast of _____.
13. Sanibel Island is off the coast of _____.
14. Cape Island is off the coast of _____.
15. Bull Island is off the coast of _____.
16. Nantucket Island is off the coast of _____.
17. Long Island is off the coast of _____.
18. Acadia is off the coast of _____.
19. The Florida Keys are off the coast of _____.
20. Staten Island is off the coast of _____.

In addition to barrier islands, mainland coastal communities that outline the Gulf of Mexico and the Atlantic Ocean also sometimes find themselves in the path of a hurricane. Circle the coastal cities below.

Hurricanes travel in a northeasternly arch and weaken into tropical storms as they move over land. Underline the cities that are likely to experience tropical storm weather.
Note: Some cities will not be underlined or circled.

NEW ORLEANS	CHICAGO	JACKSONVILLE	MADISON
ATLANTA	CORPUS CHRISTI	BIRMINGHAM	ST. PETERSBURG
NORFOLK	DETROIT	COLUMBIA	DENVER

Guarding Against the Elements

Galveston Island residents built themselves a 17-foot storm wall to protect against further hurricanes following the 1900 storm. Osaka, Japan, has done more than that! In 1961, when Osaka was ravaged by its sixth major typhoon (the eastern equivalent of a hurricane) in 30 years, it decided to take action. The city invested 16 years of labor and $560 million dollars into a unique system of embankments, barriers, pumping stations, and flood gates to combat the winds, waves, and rains of a typhoon. Read the descriptions below of the ingenious system and then draw a picture of each protective device.

A Flood Gate
An 80-foot arched tidal gate stretches over the entrance to each of the five rivers that flow into Osaka. Each gate can be lowered to the bed of the river to form a dam on 30 minutes' notice of an approaching storm.

A Water Barrier
Twenty-eight water barriers hang above small rivers and canals within the city, waiting to be dropped vertically in the event of a storm.

A Horizontally Operated Flood Gate
Other flood gates are operated horizontally so large ships can have clearance through the rivers of the city.

A Pumping Station and Drainage Canals
Flooding caused by the rains of typhoons is controlled by six pumping stations that push water into drainage channels.

Rebuilding Following Disaster

Residents of Galveston set about rebuilding their city at once following the September 8, 1900, disaster. They salvaged what wood they could from destroyed buildings and created a city anew. Imagine your town has been destroyed by a hurricane. In what order would you put things back together? Consider basic needs and health concerns as you make your decisions. Prioritize the 12 jobs presented below and justify your responses by completing the sentences provided.

Securing sanitary toilet facilities would rank _____ in my order of things to do because

_____.

Building new schools would rank _____ in my order of things to do because_____

_____.

Rebuilding stores and other businesses would rank _____ in my order of things to do because _____.

Rebuilding roads and bridges would rank _____ in my order of things to do because

_____.

Securing a temporary, reliable, outside source of water for my town's residents would rank _____ in my order of things to do because _____.

Restoring the town's own water system so residents would no longer need to rely on an outside source of water would rank _____ in my order of things to do because_____

_____.

Disposing of dead animals and people would rank _____ in my order of things to do because _____.

Securing reliable sources of food for my town's residents would rank _____ in my order of things to do because _____.

Planting new crops to ensure a future supply of food for my town's residents would rank _____ in my order of things to do because _____.

Establishing temporary shelters for the homeless would rank _____ in my order of things to do because _____.

Rebuilding residential homes and apartments would rank _____ in my order of things to do because _____.

Providing survivors of the hurricane with counseling services would rank _____ in my order of things to do because _____.

Hurricane Camille: A Party Planner's Parable

National Weather Service meteorologist Neil Frank's before-and-after slide show told the story of Hurricane Camille—a party planner's parable. Hurricane Camille developed in early August 1969 out of a tropical storm in the Caribbean Sea south of Hispaniola. Forecasters did not predict she would produce a massive inland storm because Camille's cloud pattern appeared relatively small on satellite images. Then the National Oceanic and Atmospheric Administration (NOAA) sent a plane crew into the storm while it was still at sea. Urgent reports from the NOAA scientists about the storm's wind strength and patterns, temperature, and barometric pressure level prompted the Weather Bureau to quickly upgrade its predictions. Hundreds of thousands of residents evacuated their homes just hours before Camille struck land.

Twenty-four residents at the beach front Richelieu Apartments in Pass Christian, Mississippi, did not. They planned a hurricane party instead. Since the 1950s, such parties had become popular among residents of hurricane-prone regions who found they could weather small storms with a stockpile of emergency food and water, and the spirit of a thrillseeker. But Hurricane Camille was no such small storm. Hurricane Camille was one of only two Category 5 storms to ever hit the United States.

When she hit Pass Christian, Mississippi, Hurricane Camille boasted a 24-foot storm surge and 175 m.p.h. winds. A husband and wife on the second floor of the Richelieu residence were preparing to leave their apartment and join 12 others who were already celebrating the storm on the third floor when a forceful wave crashed through their living room window. The couple ran to a bedroom and pushed hard on the door to keep out the tide, but they were overpowered. As the bedroom filled with wind and water, the wife swam through a window, and the husband was sucked under the surge. When the wife turned back, she saw the entire Richelieu Apartment building crumble to the ground under the force of the storm. The catastrophe's sole survivor grabbed hold of a piece of debris and rushed atop waves and winds all night before being deposited upon the top of a tree from which she was rescued the next morning.

Neil Frank told the story of Camille to civic groups, government officials, and reporters. He told other stories too, because he found that thousands of residents in the regions of the Atlantic seaboard and coastal communities around the Gulf of Mexico were ignorant of storms that devastated their beaches in years past. They were convinced that the curve of a coastline or a reef off shore protected them from destructive storms. Mr. Frank did not tell the residents to move. As Hurricane Center Director in the 1970s and 1980s, he only preached preparedness.

Damage reached the $1.4 billion mark. Hurricane Camille destroyed 5,500 houses and damaged 12,500 others. It covered the 26-mile Pontchartrain Causeway bridge in water. It washed three large ships ashore, and deemed 500 miles of road impassable. As it traveled inland, its rainfall caused flash flooding in the Appalachian Mountains that claimed 100 lives. All told, 256 people lost their lives in the storm. Hundreds of thousands of others survived because they heeded the warnings of Weather Bureau personnel and evacuated their homes. Neil Frank wanted to be certain people in the future would heed evacuation warnings that could someday affect their Atlantic seaboard towns. The story of Hurricane Camille reminds us why.

Elevated Warnings

Thanks to computer modeling, hurricane reconnaissance planes, and other technology, people can be warned about hurricanes in advance today. But preparing for a hurricane costs a region millions of dollars since stores close and lose business, manufacturing plants stop producing, and beach front buildings are boarded up. False warnings make residents less likely to heed future warnings. So, hurricane forecasters are careful to wait until a storm's path can be fairly well pinpointed before they issue a full-alert watch in which residents are required to evacuate an area. Match the levels of warning below with their likely purpose.

Forecasters Say That . . .

_____ 1. A storm off the coast may be headed our way.

_____ 2. A watch will likely be issued in a few hours.

_____ 3. A watch has been issued.

_____ 4. A warning has been issued.

In Order That . . .

A. Those planning to vacation in the area will postpone their trip.

B. All residents are required to evacuate.

C. Cautious individuals and those who have no pressing commitments will evacuate voluntarily.

D. Residents make necessary arrangements for possible evacuation.

In a paragraph, explain why it is important that forecasters not issue a hurricane warning until the storm is close enough that its inland path can be fairly accurately predicted.

_____

_____

_____

_____

_____

If you lived in a hurricane-prone region and you listened to the elevated levels of warning mentioned above in numbers 1-4, at which stage would *you* evacuate *your* home? Why?

_____

_____

_____

_____

What's in a Name?

Read the brief history of the naming of hurricanes below. Then place the hurricanes that follow in their proper time frame.

The History of Naming Hurricanes in America

Hurricanes that strike the Atlantic Basin are given names to expedite communication about their paths and development, but this was not always the case. Storms in early America were identified only by their latitude and longitude. The general names they were assigned which made reference to related events, places, or persons were created only after the storms had passed. So historians talk of the Charleston Hurricane of 1811 or the Benjamin Franklin Eclipse Hurricane, but those who lived through the storms knew them only by their locations.

Identifying a hurricane by its longitude and latitude became cumbersome and prone to error when radio communications and forecasting methods made it possible to warn residents of an approaching storm. So air force and navy meteorologists began identifying storms with female names during World War II. Meteorologist Clement Wragge had already begun this tradition in Australia 50 years earlier, and author George R. Stewart had, too, in his 1941 novel called *Storm*.

Still the United States weather services did not start naming storms until 1950, when they experimented with assigning names according to the phonetic alphabet (Able, Baker, Charlie, etc.). In 1953 they abandoned that failed experiment for the less confusing use of female names to identify hurricanes in America. In 1978 they added male names to the array.

Today, scientists have devised a six-year rotation of hurricane names. The first storm of a season takes on the name that begins with A for that year, the second storm takes on the name that begins with B, etc. Since the names cycle through a six-year rotation, the first four storms of the year 2000 will be called Alberto, Beryl, Chris, and Debby, just as the first four of 1994 were named. Once a hurricane has caused enormous damage, its name is retired and a new one takes its place.

Identify the proper time period for each of the following storms according to the name it claims. The first one has been done for you.

Before 1950	1950-1952	1952-1978	1978-Present
1860—Hurricane I	_____	_____	_____
_____	_____	_____	_____
_____	_____	_____	_____

Hurricane Easy	1860—Hurricane I	Hurricane Audrey
The Great Hurricane of 1780	Hurricane King	Hurricane George
Hurricane Hugo	Hurricane Able	Hurricane Mitch
The Late Gale at St. Joseph	Hurricane Hazel	Hurricane Eloise

Twentieth-Century Hurricanes

Locate the historical hurricanes in the box below in a weather or hurricane reference book or encyclopedia to help you match each with its description. The first one has been done for you.

Historical Hurricanes		
Hurricane Elena	Hurricane Agnes	Hurricane Edna
New England Hurricane of 1938	Hurricane Hugo	Hurricane Andrew
1935 Florida Keys Hurricane	Hurricane Hazel	Hurricane Fredric

___Hurricane Edna___ 1. This second storm of the 1953 season poured five inches of rain on New York City in 14 hours and left 22 people dead, but it and its predecessor, Hurricane Carol, were only preludes to the monster storm to come.

_____ 2. This Category 5 hurricane was the strongest to ever hit the United States. It devastated the Florida Keys, made landfall on the Florida mainland, weakened to a tropical storm over Georgia, and grew into hurricane status again as it passed over the North Atlantic on its way to Norfolk, Virginia.

_____ 3. Although it never grew into anything more than a Category 1 storm, this hurricane caused $2.1 billion in damage in Florida, New York, Pennsylvania, New Jersey, Delaware, and Maryland as it spawned 18 tornadoes and dumped heavy, flood-triggering rains.

_____ 4. This third and mightiest of the 1954 storms destroyed three towns in Haiti, killing about 1,000 people, and dumped heavy rains on Puerto Rico and the Bahamas before crashing upon the shore of Myrtle Beach, South Carolina, with a 17-foot surge. Its winds continued to gust at 100 m.p.h. climbing to North Carolina, Virginia, Maryland, Pennsylvania, New York, and finally Toronto, Canada.

_____ 5. This 1989 storm claimed 12 lives in Puerto Rico, and battered the U.S. Virgin Islands, before hitting a spot northwest of Charleston, South Carolina, on September 21. The Category 4 storm remained strong all the way to Charlotte, North Carolina.

_____ 6. This 1985 storm surprised forecasters who predicted its movement toward the Florida panhandle, but did not foresee its turning east toward Tampa Bay. As panhandle residents returned home and Tampa Bay residents evacuated, this storm headed back to the panhandle. Eventually, it made landfall at the Mississippi/Louisiana border.

_____ 7. Although this 1979 storm caused $2.3 billion worth of damage when it struck Alabama at the Mobile Bay, it only took five lives thanks to timely warnings well-heeded.

_____ 8. This recent Category 4 hurricane that made landfall south of Miami cost the United States more than any other natural disaster in history—$25 billion.

_____ 9. In 1938 there were no satellite images to warn residents of the coastal regions of Long Island, Connecticut, Massachusetts, and Rhode Island that they would soon be hit with a high storm surge and 70 m.p.h. winds.

Hurricane Mitch:
A Modern Mess

In January 1999, the tourism minister of Honduras issued a statement inviting foreigners to come and visit. The 15-day tour package he was offering included traditional attractions such as mountains and Mayan ruins, as well as some nontraditional stops. Mr. Norman Garcia was inviting visitors to witness first-hand the damage caused by 1998's Hurricane Mitch and to spend a few days providing medical assistance or raising a hammer and nail in helping put his country back together.

On October 22, 1998, a tropical depression had developed over the western Atlantic Ocean. Within four days, Mitch grew into a Category 5 storm. After devastating the Honduran island of Guanaja, Mitch made landfall on the mainland and then lingered. For one whole week, the storm dumped over two feet of water per day on Honduras and neighboring Nicaragua. Floods and mudslides swept entire villages away. Approximately 11,000 people lost their lives. Washed out bridges and destroyed roads made it necessary for helicopters to reach many survivors who clung to the tops of their homes for as long as a week. Two million other survivors found themselves without a home to cling to. Schools, hospitals, and government buildings were demolished. Water systems were contaminated. Crops were destroyed. Then Mitch weakened into a tropical storm, caused heavy rainfall and minor damage in Florida and her Keys, passed through the Bahamas, and dissipated. Hurricane Mitch was done with its work. The residents of Central America were just beginning theirs.

Honduras was the hardest hit of the countries affected by the hurricane. One month following the storm, 6,500 residents were counted dead and 11,000 were missing. Seventy-five percent of the roads and bridges were destroyed. One third of the buildings in the capital were demolished. Twenty-five of the northern villages were swept away. Coffee warehouses were flooded, and 70% of the nation's banana, maize, and corn crops were wiped out. Electricity was nonexistent, and food and clean drinking water were scarce.

Nicaragua fared only marginally better. The collapse of the walls of a crater lake atop a dormant volcano contributed to the 3,800 deaths and 7,000 missing persons in the country. The October 30 mudflow buried four villages when it covered an area ten miles long and five miles wide in mud. As many as 750,000 people lost their homes to the storm. Beans, sugar, and banana crops were destroyed. Thousands of landmines left over from a 1980s civil war were unearthed and scattered across rural communities.

El Salvador, Guatemala, Costa Rica, Belize, and Mexico reported deaths and damages as well.

Putting Central America back together again will not be easy. The president of Honduras suggested the storm destroyed 50 years of progress. Relief workers and government officials predict it will take two or more decades to rebuild the region's infrastructure. Government and nongovernmental organizations from around the globe are assisting in the effort. UNICEF is providing and distributing food, safe drinking water, cooking utensils, medicines, and blankets to homeless refugees in immediate need. The United States Geological Survey is providing scientific and technological expertise to help ensure rebuilt communities will be less susceptible to future storms.

The Great Hurricane of 1780

Only one hurricane in the last two centuries has been more powerful and destructive than Hurricane Mitch. The Great Hurricane claimed 22,000 lives in the eastern Caribbean in the year 1780. Use logic and your understanding of sentence structure to combine the first and second half of the sentences below as you learn about the Great Hurricane of 1780. The two halves of the first sentence have been combined for you.

1. The Great Hurricane was the second of . . . __D__.
2. Barbados was the first . . . _____.
3. The captains of many ships who witnessed the destruction of the hurricane after the fact concluded from the massive destruction . . . _____.
4. The massive destruction caused by recent hurricanes suggests . . . _____.
5. A letter from the governor of Barbados published in the *London Gazette* described . . . _____.
6. A press dispatch from St. Vincent, the second island to be hit by the storm, stated that . . . _____.
7. An account from the island of Grenada reported that . . . _____.
8. The *St. Lucia Gazette* told of the fate of ships caught in the storm when it stated that . . . _____.
9. Thousands of people on and around the French island of Martinique died including . . . _____.
10. A local press report from the island of Dominica suggested the hurricane lingered over it for 24 hours from . . . _____.
11. The Great Hurricane of 1780 finally lost its force . . . _____.

A. . . . island to feel the effects of the Great Hurricane.
B. . . . the earthquake theory was probably false.
C. . . . "of 600 houses (in St. Vincent's Kingstown) there remained only 14 standing, following the hurricane that continued for twenty-four hours without intermission."
D. . . . eight damaging storms to batter West Indian and American waters in 1780.
E. . . . that an earthquake must have hit the island of Barbados along with the hurricane.
F. . . . 3,000 French soldiers who were on their way to the island aboard ships, 1,000 residents of the city of St. Pieffe, and 100 in the town of Notre Dame.
G. . . . after driving ashore 50 ships on the Bermuda Island, where it experienced its last reported surge.
H. . . . the devastation on his island, stating that trees were torn up by the roots and not a building was left standing.
I. . . . nineteen Dutch ships had been stranded on her shores and "beat to pieces."
J. . . . noon of the first day when rain and thunder became violent to noon of the next day when the storm "finished the destruction of everything that resisted it."
K. . . . "there was scarce a vessel left in the road [that hadn't] drifted, and many were on shore or carried with astonishing force against the other [ships]."

Hurricane Heroes

Look for hints in the descriptions on the left of "hurricane heroes" to help you match each with a name on the right.

_____ 1. As director of the National Hurricane Center in the early 1970s, this man developed a scale to measure hurricane damage along with Herbert Saffir. Some 30 years earlier this man admired the forecasting abilities of Grady Norton.

A. Herbert Saffir

B. Robert Simpson

C. Colonel Joseph B. Duckworth

_____ 2. On July 27, 1944, this Army Air Force colonel, a flight and instrument instructor, became the first man to fly a plane directly into a hurricane.

D. Grady Norton

E. Neil Frank

F. Lieutenant Ralph O'Hair

_____ 3. The chief of the U.S. Weather Bureau from 1935 to 1945 became famous for his accurate path predictions of storms originating in the Gulf of Mexico and Atlantic Oceans. In addition to using the available technology of his day, he relied on a keen intuitive insight in making his predictions. When Robert Simpson asked him how he knew a 1944 storm would make a sudden northward turn that no one else could have guessed, he commented that he watched the clouds outside his office window and "usually, the answer comes to me."

_____ 4. This Houston, Texas, weatherman—and later director of the National Hurricane Center—was as frank as his name in educating the public about the destructive powers of a hurricane.

_____ 5. This Army Air Force lieutenant acted as the navigator during the first intentional flight into a hurricane on July 27, 1944.

_____ 6. This authority on designing buildings to withstand hurricanes added an engineer's point of view to the meteorological views of Robert Simpson in developing the Saffir-Simpson Hurricane Damage Scale.

World Community Volunteers

When Hurricane Mitch smashed into South America, over one million people's lives and property were affected. The tragedy was so all-encompassing that the affected nations were not even able to make the outside world aware of the extent of the damages for over a week. Communication systems, crops, roads, bridges, schools, and homes had been annihilated. Whole villages had been swept away. The president of Honduras claimed that 50 years of progress had been destroyed.

When the world did comprehend the extent of the disaster, it responded immediately. Churches, charities, and individuals sent money to South American governments. The World Food Bank organized the distribution of food and water to hundreds of thousands of people. Red Cross and United Nations workers set up shelters and administered first-aid. Governments around the globe forgave some of the international debt owed by affected nations. Geologists, scientists, doctors, and construction workers flew in from around the world to offer expertise and help to rebuild cities and restore livelihoods. The volunteers may not have renewed the hurricane region's 50 years of progress, but they accomplished the seemingly insurmountable task of putting communities back together.

With a group of three or four students, consider the following questions. Record your group responses on a separate sheet of paper. If time permits, compare your responses with those of other groups.

1. Politicians, organizations, and civilians set aside their differences to assist victims and restore peace, health, and normalcy to any nation devastated by a natural disaster. Why do they not make that same effort for the victims of war or civil unrest?
2. Social progress sometimes takes years to accomplish. Quakers and other concerned citizens were voicing opposition to slavery in 1787 when the Constitution was being written. Still slavery was not abolished until 1865. Imagine how quickly changes could be achieved by organizations and individuals if people concentrated as much effort and set aside differences as quickly for social concerns as they do to restore a region following a natural disaster. Could human beings maintain such harmony and intense efforts over an extended period of time?
3. Why do natural disasters bring out the instinct to help?
4. Since natural disasters are often unexpected events, efforts to provide relief often contain loose and makeshift organization. In nonemergency situations, is it possible to accomplish more when a hierarchy of organization is firmly established or when people make spur-of-the-moment decisions based on immediate needs?
5. Is there any social issue you feel deserves the concentrated attention of world leaders and everyday citizens today?

The Tri-State Tornado: Most Deadly Tornado in National History

Unlike hurricanes, tornadoes are not massive storms that carve out damage paths hundreds of miles long. Tornadoes are small, concentrated funnels (seldom over a few hundred yards in width) that travel an average of just six miles and typically last no longer than 15 minutes. Only two percent of all tornadoes travel paths in excess of 30 miles. Only a half percent traverse more than 100 miles. Yet on March 18, 1925, a thunderstorm near Redford, Missouri, spawned a mile-wide tornado that lived for three and one-half hours and traveled 219 miles.

The F5 magnitude Tri-State Tornado raced north from Redford, Missouri, at a varying speed of 60-73 miles per hour, crossing the Mississippi River southeast of St. Louis, speeding into southern Illinois, and finally dissipating in southwestern Indiana. In its wake, it left 695 people dead and 2,000 injured, making it the deadliest tornado in the history of the United States.

Like the death and destruction caused by most tornadoes, the Tri-State tornado damage was uneven and random. In rural areas, untouched farmhouses and grain silos stood beside completely demolished corn fields. In urban areas, a few select office buildings stood undamaged amidst the rubble of otherwise completely destroyed business districts. In residential neighborhoods, streets lined with piles of wood, glass, and overturned houses on one side were faced with tranquil intact homes on the other. During the three-and-a-half hour attack, eight people were killed in Missouri towns: four in Annapolis and four in Biehle. Seventy people died in Indiana communities: 25 in Griffin and 45 in Princeton. Five hundred and eighty-eight people lost their lives in southern Illinois towns. And another 129 people died throughout the three states' rural regions.

The death toll from the Tri-State Tornado was high for three reasons. First, in 1925 there was no organized warning system to inform residents of an approaching tornado. Second, the tornado covered a path that paralleled a network of railroad tracks which served populated industrial towns and commercial communities. Finally, the Tri-State Tornado traveled in disguise. Witnesses described the funnel as a black, low, rumbling cloud. Most observers prepared only for a severe thunderstorm. Victims did not know a tornado threatened until they were actually hit with its debris.

Today, meteorologists can warn residents when weather conditions are conducive to the formation of tornadoes. They can tell citizens when a tornado has been sighted in their area. If people react quickly to tornado warnings, they can substantially increase their chances of staying safe.

Watches and Warnings

Today the Weather Bureau's tornado warning system keeps the death toll down during tornado attacks. What do you do when a tornado watch (which warns of conditions suitable to the production of tornadoes) turns into a tornado warning indicating that a twister has been sighted in your area? Remember, you have very little time. With our limited understanding of tornadoes, 20 minutes' warning is the best forecasters can give. Write *true* or *false* in the blanks below to indicate your response at the issuance of a tornado warning.

_____ 1. If you are indoors, you seek shelter in the lowest level of the building.

_____ 2. If you are in a home without a basement, you lie flat on the floor anywhere inside the building.

_____ 3. If possible, you cover your head and eyes with a jacket or blanket to protect them from flying debris.

_____ 4. If you are inside a mobile home, you sit with your back against an inside wall and cover your head.

_____ 5. If you are outside, you seek a ditch or low-lying area in which to lie.

_____ 6. If you are in a car, you stop it, get out, and seek a ditch in which to lie.

_____ 7. If you are in a building that appears to be in the path of an approaching tornado, you get out, jump in your car, and drive quickly to a safer location.

_____ 8. If you are in public, and it is possible, you seek a wide-open building like a mall or gymnasium to shelter you.

Before and After

Optimum safety in the event of any storm requires not only that you know what to do in the event of a warning, but also that you make some prior preparations and know how to respond after a storm has passed. In the spaces provided, write *B* for *before* or *A* for *after* to indicate when you would complete each safety activity described.

_____ 1. Determine the options your insurance company provides in case of property losses caused by a storm.

_____ 2. Stay away from downed power lines.

_____ 3. Evacuate your home if you smell gas or fumes.

_____ 4. Learn the incident rate of tornadoes in your area.

_____ 5. Know your town's plan for emergencies.

_____ 6. Prepare a disaster kit complete with battery-operated radio, flashlight, extra batteries, water, food, first aid kit, clothing, and bedding.

_____ 7. Clean up dangerous chemical spills immediately.

_____ 8. To prevent fires, use flashlights rather than candles.

_____ 9. Formulate a family disaster plan that includes communication plans, evacuation plans, and plans for places to meet after a tornado passes.

_____10. Do not enter damaged buildings.

_____11. Wait for a message from the weather service before leaving your place of shelter. Tornadoes sometimes strike in pairs—or in even greater numbers!

Famous Funnels

Locate information about the following tornadoes on the Internet or in a tornado resource book to help you match each with its description below. Write the number in the blank.

_____ Great Natchez Tornado of May 1840

_____ Great Southern Tornado Outbreak of 1884

_____ Worcester County, Massachusetts, Tornado of 1953

_____ May 1948 Tornado of McKinney, Texas

_____ Viroqua, Wisconsin, Tornado: June 28, 1865

_____ Hurricane Beulah

_____ Kansas Turnpike Tornado

1. Sixty or more tornadoes struck tenant farms and small plantations in Mississippi, Alabama, Georgia, Tennessee, South Carolina, North Carolina, and Virginia, when this outbreak killed an estimated 800 people in the states' rural areas.

2. Captain Roy S. Hall wrote his account of looking directly into this tornado and seeing and hearing "vivid lightning and rending crashes."

3. Three hundred and seventeen people lost their lives, and $1 million in property damages was incurred when this tornado struck an active port in Mississippi destroying flatboats, commercial buildings, and homes. This natural disaster has been called the greatest pre-Civil War American storm disaster in terms of death and destruction.

4. The New England residents struck by this tornado were shocked by the occurrence both because there were no public warnings of the tornado and because tornadoes are so uncommon to their region. Many victims injured by the tornado reported that they had not seen it approaching. Others stated they saw the funnel, but did not recognize it as a tornado. None of the interviewed survivors recognized the large hail that preceded the tornado as a sign of impending danger, and none of them received any official warning of the storm.

5. County Clerk John M. Bennett wrote about his family's experience with this tornado, which included an early fascination with the storm and a last-minute rush to the cellar. Results of the storm included a horse being carried 1,000 feet through the air to land directly in front of Mr. Bennett and flying debris including splinters, dust, and tufts of fleece from a demolished farm storage building swirling through the air. Seven children and a teacher died when this tornado left the Bennett home and touched down atop a schoolhouse that stood in an open prairie two miles away.

6. This tornado was made famous by the television crew that filmed its progression from underneath a highway bridge.

7. This 1967 hurricane spawned 115 tornadoes in the southeastern part of Texas from September 19 through September 23.

Winning Arguments

Write a persuasive essay based on one of the following topics.

1. Hurricanes affect much larger regions than do tornadoes, causing much greater destruction. Convince your reader that hurricanes are more ferocious than tornadoes.

2. Tornadoes, which have been labeled terrorists, strike randomly and with little warning. Scientists still know only enough about their formation to give citizens a maximum of 20 minutes' warning of their approach. Buildings cannot be constructed to withstand the 300 m.p.h. winds of an F5 tornado. Convince your reader that tornadoes are more ferocious than hurricanes.

3. Scientists suggest that tornadoes work to rid the atmosphere of excess heat. Research global warming and then convince your reader that the increase in the number of tornadoes that hit the United States each year might be correlated to global warming.

4. Tornado Alley, which includes parts of Texas, Kansas, and Oklahoma, attracts the most tornadoes in the United States, but there is no place on earth that is completely safe from a tornado. Convince your reader that preparedness is the best defense in the event of a tornado striking. Include information on emergency plans and supplies and adhering to warnings.

_____

_____

_____

_____

_____

_____

_____

_____

_____

_____

_____

_____

_____

_____

_____

_____

Name _____

A Blizzard A'Blowin'

Tornadoes and hurricanes are not the only storms that produce fierce winds. Blizzards drive sheets of snow sideways at 35–75 miles per hour. Place each of the following American Red Cross suggestions about dealing with winter storms under the appropriate heading below. The first one has been placed for you.

Home Preparations   Staying Informed

1. _____   _____

Travel Preparations   If You Get Stranded in a Car

_____   _____

1. Have extra blankets on hand.
2. Listen to radio and television updates on storm information.
3. Avoid travel if possible when a winter storm warning has been issued.
4. Prepare to stay indoors during a winter storm if possible.
5. Stay with your car. Do not try to walk to safety.
6. Understand the hazards of wind chill, which combines the cooling effect of wind and cold temperatures on exposed skin.
7. Assemble a disaster supply kit for your home.
8. Assemble a disaster supply kit for your car.
9. Know that several layers of lightweight clothing will keep you warmer than a single heavy coat. Also be informed that gloves and a hat will prevent loss of body heat, and covering your mouth will protect your lungs.
10. Tie a brightly colored cloth to the antenna for rescuers to see.
11. Start the car and use the heater for about ten minutes every hour. Keep the exhaust pipes clear so fumes will not back up into your car.
12. Ensure that each member of your household has a warm coat, gloves or mittens, hat, and water-resistant boots.
13. Let someone know your destination, your route, and when you expect to arrive.
14. Leave the overhead light on when the engine is running so you can be seen.
15. Know that a winter storm watch means a winter storm is possible in your area. A winter storm warning means a winter storm is headed your way. A blizzard warning means strong winds, blinding wind-driven snow, and dangerous wind chills are expected. Seek shelter immediately!
16. As you sit, keep moving your arms and legs to keep blood circulating and to keep warm.
17. Keep your car's gas tank full for emergency use.
18. Keep one window away from the blowing wind slightly open to let in air.
19. Order American Red Cross videos and publications to broaden your knowledge on how to survive the cold and prepare for winter weather.

The 1974 Super Outbreak: The 148 Tornadoes of a Single Storm System

In any given year, between 500 and 1,000 tornadoes strike the United States. In any given decade, an average of 5 of those tornadoes are classified as magnitude F5 events. Over the course of 16 hours in the spring of 1974, the averages were drastically upset when a single storm system spawned 148 tornadoes that ripped through 13 midwestern states and one Canadian province. The winds of six of the storm's tornadoes reached the speed of 261 miles per hour or more, designating them F5 tornadoes.

The 1974 Super Outbreak was the most damaging tornado outbreak in the history of the nation. An F5 tornado destroyed the entire town of Guin, Alabama, killing 20. Another F5 tornado devastated Brandenburg, Kentucky, killing 30. Six communities were struck by two separate funnel clouds. A twister that hit Louisville, Kentucky, destroyed 900 homes in 20 minutes over the course of the storm's lifespan. The 148 tornadoes that made their way through 13 states from Alabama and Georgia north to Michigan and into Canada beginning in the late afternoon of April 3 and continuing into the early morning of April 4, covered tracks averaging 18.7 miles each, slashing a total path of 2,598 miles. As the fierce winds blew, freight cars of a passing train were transported across the street, trees and telephone poles were bent to the ground, and chunks of roof, wall, and window were transformed into high speed missiles of destruction. Three hundred and fifteen people lost their lives to the outbreak, 5,484 were injured, and 27,590 suffered property loss.

At 4:25 p.m., only 16 students and one teacher remained in the Central High School building in Xenia, Ohio, when one of the most destructive funnels of the storm reached their community. At first the students ran from the stage where they had been rehearsing for a school play to a nearby window to get a glance of what they expected to be a far-off funnel. When they caught sight, instead, of cars flying through the parking lot, they immediately sought shelter. Huddling in the center of the building with their backs against an inside wall, the students heard a screaming, whistling noise and watched chunks of dirt, glass, and wood fly horizontally through the hallway in front of them for what seemed like an eternity. When the winds finally subsided, the students and their teacher sat in a roofless structure. On the stage of the drama room, where they had been rehearsing just four minutes earlier, sat two overturned buses, testifying to the power of the storm they had all survived.

Although not nearly as long-lasting or as far-reaching as hurricanes, tornadoes—producing the fastest winds found on the planet—can achieve a remarkable degree of damage in a remarkably short period of time.

Reading the Sky

Knowing the characteristics of cloud types helps meteorologists recognize the conditions associated with the formation of thunderstorms and tornadoes. Use a weather reference book or your science textbook to help you identify the following cloud types. Then draw a picture of each type in the space provided.

Cloud Types

Cirrus	Cumulus	Stratus	Cirrocumulus	Cumulonimbus
	Nimbostratus	Altocumulus	Stratocumulus	Altostratus

1. These low clouds, also known as fog, blanket the sky.

   _____

2. These feathery, thread-like clouds are located high in the sky.

   _____

3. These high clouds create a row of small, white, wispy balls.

   _____

4. These thin, soft, rolling clouds sometimes cover the entire sky.

   _____

5. This puffy, white cloud with a flat base looks like cauliflower.

   _____

6. These dark, heavy clouds are also known as thunderclouds.

   _____

7. These low-level clouds are thick, dark, and shapeless.

   _____

8. These medium-level clouds produce large, puffy balls.

   _____

9. These medium-level clouds produce a thick, bluish veil.

   _____

Tornadoes In Verse

The multiple suction vortexes that form in some tornadoes can play freakish tricks on the people and things in their paths. Concentrated twisters within a twister can destroy one half of a house and leave the other half untouched. They can wrap cars around telephone poles or transport victims several miles by air before dropping them to safety. The wreckage after a tornado can include defeathered chickens, twisted light poles, and pieces of straw stuck firmly into large old trees.

Following a 1973 tornado, a Blue Springs, Nebraska, man would have to walk to the center of his cornfield to play the piano that once sat in his living room. Following a 1974 tornado in Madison, Indiana, a completely intact closet wherein huddled a family stood upright and untouched beside the rubble that was the rest of the family's house.

Create three poems about the chaos tornadoes can create following the formats described below. Sample poems have been devised for you.

Tornado Haiku

A three-lined poem in which the first line has 5 syllables, the second line has 7 syllables, and the third line has 5 syllables.

Sample Poem	*Your Poem*
Defeathered chickens	_____
Twisted, downed telephone poles	_____
Tornadoes tonight	_____

Tornado Couplet
A two-lined rhyming poem.

Sample Poem	*Your Poem*
Tornadoes make winds whirl	_____
And cows twirl	_____

Tornado Limerick
A humorous, five-lined poem in which lines one, two, and five rhyme with one another and lines three and four rhyme with each other.

Sample Poem	*Your Poem*
A tornado once tore through my home	_____
The darned thing wouldn't leave me alone	_____
It swallowed my cat	_____
And sported my hat	_____
Took my dog and left me with his bone	_____

Worthwhile Wind

Although the 40–318 m.p.h. winds of a tornado might be unpleasant, a less strong breeze can be quite useful to human beings. Indicate below how the following items make use of air. The first one has been done for you.

1. Windmill: _harnesses the energy of the wind to create power that is converted into_ _electricity_

2. Vacuum Cleaner: _____
   _____

3. Water Pumps: _____
   _____

4. Boat Sail: _____
   _____

5. Air Drills: _____
   _____

6. Air Brakes: _____
   _____

7. Sand Blasters: _____
   _____

8. Spray Bottles: _____
   _____

9. Parachutes: _____
   _____

10. Basketball: _____
    _____

11. Spores and Seeds: _____
    _____

12. Brass and Wind Instruments: _____
    _____

13. Airplane Wings: _____
    _____

14. Sunset: _____
    _____

15. Hot Air Balloons: _____
    _____

Knowing the Numbers

Complete the math problems below to discover statistics based on the ranking of states hit by tornadoes from 1950–1994.

1. From the years 1950–1994, Texas experienced more tornadoes than any other state, incurring more fatalities, more injuries, and more damage costs. Complete the problems below to determine the numbers.

   A. _____ tornadoes hit Texas from 1950-1994.

   B. Texas suffered _____ fatalities from the tornadoes.

   C. _____ people were injured by the twisters in Texas.

   D. The tornadoes cost Texas over _____ million dollars.

   A. $4{,}099 + 1{,}391 =$

   B. 4.75×10^2

   C. $(5^2 \times 20) + (321 \times 18) + 1{,}174 =$

   D. $\sqrt{363 - 2} =$

2. Although Indiana ranks fifteenth in the number of tornadoes that hit its state between 1950 and 1994, it ranks second in damage costs. Determine the numbers below.

   A. _____ tornadoes hit Indiana from 1950–1994. This is the same number of tornadoes that hit Alabama during the same time period.

   B. The tornadoes cost Indiana over _____ million dollars in damages.

   A. $2(360 + 83) =$

   B. $197.28 \div 12.33 =$

3. The District of Columbia was hit by few enough tornadoes from 1950 to 1994 to be ranked last in the nation in number of tornadoes experienced for the time period.

   A. The District of Columbia experienced _____ tornadoes during the time period.

   A. $1{,}453{,}278 \times 0 =$

4. Although nearly 100 tornadoes hit Maine during the time period, it suffered very few deaths. Determine the numbers.

   A. _____ tornadoes hit Maine from 1950–1994.

   B. _____ person(s) died as a result of the natural disasters.

   A. $100 - 75 + 25 + 32 - 14 + 14 =$

   B. $\sqrt{64} - 7 =$

5. Fewer than 100 people were injured in tornadoes that occurred in California from 1950–1994. Determine exactly how many.

   A. _____ people were injured in California tornadoes during the time period.

   A. $3^4 + 2 =$

Life-Threatening Droughts

What Is a Drought?

A drought is a period of abnormally dry weather that lasts long enough to cause an imbalance in the hydrologic cycle—the continual flow of water from the ocean to the atmosphere to the land and back to the ocean. Droughts can be classified according to the normal conditions of the climates they affect. Permanent droughts exist in regions where the climate is already excessively dry. Seasonal droughts exist in regions that experience seasonally dry conditions. Contingent droughts exist in regions where rain is normally expected, but does not fall for a long period of time. Invisible droughts exist in regions where the moisture lost by crops through evaporation is not counterbalanced with adequate precipitation.

Where Do Droughts Occur?

Permanent droughts occur in the regions lying just north and south of the equator where moist, tropical air becomes hotter and drier as it descends to the earth. Contingent droughts can occur anywhere, but most often affect areas bordering permanent drought regions, clustering in latitudes between 15 and 20 North and South. Countries that are prone to drought include West Africa, South Africa, Brazil, Australia, and India. The Great Plains of America experienced so many dry seasons during the seventeenth through the nineteenth centuries that old maps label the entire region "The Great American Desert."

Why Do Droughts Occur?

Droughts are completely natural events. They occur because of variations in wind patterns, ocean currents, and ocean water temperatures. In some cases, a belt of winds called *the prevailing westerlies* shifts poleward, and areas that would otherwise receive wet, low-pressure weather experience high-pressure arid conditions. In other cases, disturbances in the jet stream produce atmospheric patterns that result in drought. The atmospheric changes that accompany El Niños have been associated with droughts in southeast Africa. In North America, researchers have correlated droughts with the phenomenon of sun spots and identified a 22-year cycle of dry conditions.

Why Are Droughts Disastrous?

Droughts result in crop losses, depleted soil moisture, and reduced streamflow and groundwater supplies. During a drought, harsh dust storms cut through the air at up to 40 m.p.h., and fires devastate parched prairies and dry timber. Long-term and recurrent droughts create economic hardships, fresh water shortages, and famines. Crops dry up, animals die of thirst, and people starve or become refugees.

Can Droughts Be Predicted or Prevented?

Scientists from weather services worldwide monitor climate changes, keeping track of precipitation and the moisture and nutrient content in soils. Recognizing patterns in historical records allows them to predict when a drier-than-usual season is approaching a region. Experts predicted that Mozambique and Ethiopia would experience drought conditions two years prior to their 1984 extended dry spells.

Droughts cannot be prevented, but their effects can be substantially minimized. Overcropping, overgrazing, and deforestation deplete the soil of its natural nutrients and make it less capable of retaining moisture. Residents in drought-prone regions can practice modern farming techniques to minimize the dust storms of droughts. They can also build reservoirs, store grain reserves, dig wells, and create irrigation systems so that people and animals can continue to get adequate food and water when droughts hit.

Defining Droughts

Drought is a relative term, and scientists do not agree on a single definition for the word. Read some of the *drought* definitions below and then answer the questions that follow.

Drought Definition #1: Wayne Palmer of the National Weather Service devised a drought index that compares precipitation and stored soil moisture with evaporation and a region's requirements for moisture. According to a formula, the drought index defines a water balance between -2 and +2 as normal, a balance between -2 and -3 as a moderate drought, a balance between -3 and -4 as a severe drought, and a balance of 4 or below as an extreme drought.

Drought Definition #2: Scientists in Great Britain define an absolute drought as a period of 15 consecutive days in which each day received less than .01 inches of rain. They consider 29 consecutive days with a mean daily average rainfall less than .01 a partial drought.

Drought Definition #3: In India a drought is declared when the annual rainfall is 75% less than average.

Drought Definition #4: Libya does not declare a drought until it has experienced no rain for two years.

Drought Definition #5: The Swedish hydrologist Malin Falkenmark created the following definition of dry climates: Aridity—permanently dry climate
Drought—irregularly dry climate
Desiccation—dry soils due to overgrazing and deforestation
Water Stress—water shortages due to a growing population
relying on a fixed supply of run-off water

Drought Definition #6: One operational definition of *drought* categorizes a dry spell into its effects, defining a meteorological drought according to degree and duration of dryness, an agricultural drought as one that affects agriculture, a hydrological drought as one that affects the hydrologic system, and a socioeconomic drought as one that affects supply and demand of commodities necessary to human life.

1. Which two definitions would be most helpful in directing national policy on agriculture and population growth? _____

2. Which definition would be most helpful to scientists who wish to quantify drought seasons for comparative purposes? _____

3. Which definition would probably be most simply explained to everyday citizens? _____

4. Which definition considers dry conditions a drought only if those conditions are abnormal to a region? _____

5. Which definition associates a specific quantity of rainfall with the term *drought*? _____

6. Which definition considers how much rainfall an area needs in determining the existence of a drought? _____

7. Which three definitions consider the length of a dry spell in their definitions of drought? _____

8. Which definition considers the causes of a region's dry spells and water shortages? _____

Horrifyingly Hot

Droughts are often accompanied by extremely hot temperatures. What do you know about living with extreme heat? See if you can finish the sentences below based on information provided by FEMA, the national program to inform citizens about emergency situations.

1. Extreme heat can kill a human being because_____

   _____

2. Three causes of heat illnesses are _____

3. Extreme heat is defined as _____

4. Heat disorders include _____

5. The most likely victims of heat illnesses are_____

6. Approximately _____ Americans die from extreme heat each year.

7. Men are more susceptible to heat illnesses than women because _____

   _____

8. Having a sunburn can increase your risk of heat stroke because _____

   _____

9. People living in cities may feel the effects of a heat wave before those living in rural areas because _____

10. Residents of regions that get hot in the summer should keep their storm windows on because _____

11. Outdoor awnings can reduce the heat that enters a house by _____percent.

12. Air conditioning is more effective in keeping a room cool than are electric fans because electric fans just _____

13. Drinking more liquids when it is hot outside helps your body ward off dehydration, but alcoholic beverages are not a good choice because _____

    _____

14. The best attire for beating the heat is _____

15. Never take a cool shower after coming in from the heat because _____

    _____

16. The best treatment for a sunburn is _____

17. Spasms in leg and stomach muscles related to being overheated are called _____

    _____

18. The signs of heat exhaustion are _____

    _____

19. The symptoms of heat stroke are _____

    _____

20. The treatment for heat stroke is_____

    _____

Hot and Dry Verbiage

Use a science textbook, encyclopedia, or dictionary to help you define in complete sentences the following terms having to do with droughts, heat spells, and the hydrologic cycle.

1. *Hydrologic Cycle:* _____

   _____

2. *Aquifer:* _____

   _____

3. *Desertification:* _____

   _____

4. *Black Blizzard:* _____

   _____

5. *Desiccate:* _____

   _____

6. *Deforestation:* _____

   _____

7. *Arid:* _____

   _____

8. *Dry Spell:* _____

   _____

9. *Arable Land:* _____

   _____

10. *Overcropping:* _____

    _____

11. *Ground Water:* _____

    _____

12. *Runoff:* _____

    _____

13. *Dirty Thirties:* _____

    _____

14. *Famine:* _____

    _____

15. *Maelstrom:* _____

    _____

Waste Not, Want Not

During periods of drought, affected residents are asked to cut back on the use of water in their own homes. How can one family's water decisions make a difference? Routine activities that you perform every day require a lot of water! Toilet flushing alone accounts for 28% of indoor water use. Match the activities below with the amount of water each uses on the average. Then write a sentence about how you could complete the task in a way that would conserve water. The first one has been done for you.

Average Amount of Water Used

25 gallons	14 gallons	5-7 gallons	35 gallons
10 gallons	60 gallons	20 gallons	45 gallons	2 gallons

__5-7 gallons__ 1. One flush of the toilet To conserve water install a low-capacity toilet, place a brick or an empty half gallon jug in the storage tank of your toilet, or flush less often. _____

_____ 2. Brushing your teeth _____

_____ 3. Washing dishes by hand under running water _____

_____ 4. Running the automatic dishwasher one time_____

_____ 5. Washing one load of clothes in the washing machine _____

_____ 6. Taking a bath_____

_____ 7. Taking a shower _____

_____ 8. Shaving _____

_____ 9. Washing hands _____

Dust Bowl Days: When the Rain Followed Not the Plow

In 1862 the Congress of the United States of America passed a law intended to expedite the development of the West. The Homestead Act stated that anyone willing to cultivate 160 acres west of Tennessee for at least five years would receive a deed to the property for free. The offer was eagerly accepted by one million pioneers who were motivated by a promise that in Kansas and Nebraska "the rain followed the plow." For 25 years, the new residents of the Great Plains states erected fences and sod houses, and dug up the grasses and shrubs of the prairie to cultivate the rich soil beneath their roots. No homesteader comprehended that the plentiful rains that fell on his fields were part of a temporary weather pattern that was extremely uncharacteristic for the region.

Then in 1887 the rains stopped falling, the dust started blowing, and the homesteaders began to worry—and rightly so. The late nineteenth-century drought lasted nine years. Maps began to label the Great Plains region the Great American Desert. By 1896 over half of the region's homesteaders left their free lands and returned to the East or ventured farther west into Nevada and California.

Weather records indicate that the Great Plains region has suffered drought conditions approximately every 22 years since the nine-year dry spell that chased away so many homesteaders in the late 1800s. But none has equaled the magnitude of the drought that devastated the region in the 1930s.

The dust bowl has been dubbed the greatest meteorological disaster in the history of the United States. States from Texas to Canada suffered lack of rain. A region of 150,000 square miles encompassing the Oklahoma and Texas panhandles and parts of Colorado, New Mexico, and Kansas suffered drought conditions for the whole decade.

The effects of the drought were dramatic. Without the complex root systems of the shrubs and grasses that had been plowed away from the prairie, hot winds picked up tons of topsoil and blew it across the nation. The first major storm in May of 1934 lifted 350 million tons of topsoil and dropped it on the eastern United States. Dust was detected on ships 300 miles out in the Atlantic, and dirt that reached the jet stream made its way as far as Europe. In 1932 the weather bureau reported 14 dust storms in the dust bowl region. In 1933 it reported 32 storms. By 1934 black blizzards were occurring with such alarming frequency that local residents were afraid to attend church services or visit neighbors for fear they would be caught in the zero visibility, 1,000-foot-high black clouds of an unpredictable dust storm. By 1938 the top five inches of soil had disappeared from 10 million acres, and 850 million tons of soil were blown away annually.

Plants, animals, and people suffered the effects of the drought. Small birds, whose wings tired of fighting blowing dust, fell to the ground. Jackrabbits breathed in enough dirt to line their stomachs two inches deep. Wheat and corn plants withered in the heat, bent in the wind, and became buried in the dust that struck them. People became inflicted with headaches, stomachaches, chapped skin, and "dust pneumonia." Respiratory diseases rose by 25% in the region, and infant mortality rose by a third.

Thousands of defeated families gathered their dreams and belongings in burlap bags and headed to California to find work as migrant farmers. Dust bowlers who remained wore goggles and scarves when they ventured outside. They hung wet blankets in front of their doors and lined their window frames with rags. Women learned to store water in Mason jars and knead bread inside kitchen drawers to protect it from the fine dust that made its way through the rags and wet blankets. Men of the dust bowl harvested thistles to feed their cattle and stubbornly continued to work their dry, barren fields.

Finally, in 1940 rain fell in the Great Plains. Farsighted survivors built dams, established food reserves, and planted trees, grasses, and shrubs in preparation for the next dry spell. In the 1950s, when the next drought did occur, the Great American Desert was less vulnerable.

Respecting the Water Cycle

There are 340 million cubic miles of water on the earth, all of which rotates through a cycle of runoff, storage, evaporation, and precipitation. Read about each of the steps in the cycle below and then draw a picture to illustrate the movement of a single drop of water through the entire cycle.

Steps of the Water Cycle

Runoff: Water above and under the ground flows into rivers that flow into oceans at the rate of 24 cubic miles per day.

Storage: Water in the storage level of the water cycle is located in lakes, rivers, oceans, ice caps, glaciers, and even the ground.

Evaporation: Stored water is eventually evaporated into the atmosphere as water vapor and then condenses again in clouds. Air temperature, sun intensity, wind speed, plant coverage, and ground moisture all affect the rate of water evaporation.

Precipitation: Rain, snow, ice, and hail reintroduce evaporated water into the first step of the water cycle.

A Drop of Water Moves Through the Water Cycle

Human beings alter the movement of water through the cycle in numerous ways—some of which create disastrous effects as did the short-sighted removal of prairie grasses in the dust bowl region. Describe the purpose and negative consequences of each of the water-altering actions below.

Action	Purpose	Consequence
1. Construction of irrigation ditches		
2. Pumping of water from wells		
3. Building of dams and levees		
4. Paving of roads and parking lots		
5. Removal of trees from forests		
6. Seeding clouds with water		

Roosevelt to the Rescue

In your history textbook or on the Internet, research the following New Deal acts that affected farmers during the 1930s. In an effectively organized paragraph, tell how each act assisted dust bowl farmers of the Great Plains.

Agricultural Adjustment Act of 1933

_____
_____
_____
_____

Emergency Farm Mortgage Act of 1933

_____
_____
_____
_____

Resettlement Administration Act of 1935

_____
_____
_____
_____

Soil Conservation Act of 1936

_____
_____
_____
_____

Farm Security Administration of 1937

_____
_____
_____
_____

Manifest Destiny

Many pioneers settling in the Great Plains during the late nineteenth and early twentieth centuries believed it was their right to establish homesteads in the region because it was "God's will" that Europeans develop the entire North American continent from coast to coast. But homesteaders were not the first to claim Great Plains property. Cowboys and ranchers allowed their cattle to roam free before homesteaders erected their fences. Trappers caught animals for the fur trade in the region before ranchers arrived. Native Americans used the lands as hunting grounds before the arrival of the trappers. Which group of people had the most legitimate claim to the region? Which group of people treated the land of the region with the most respect? Write an essay arguing your position.

_____

_____

_____

_____

_____

_____

_____

_____

_____

_____

_____

_____

_____

_____

_____

_____

_____

_____

Conserving the Soil

Research the role of the agricultural expert Hugh Bennett in promoting soil conservation in the Great Plains region. Record your findings here:

_____

_____

_____

_____

_____

_____

_____

Now match the soil conservation techniques that follow with their descriptions below.

_____ 1. Land Zoning   _____ 4. Contour Farming

_____ 2. Crop Rotating   _____ 5. Strip Cropping

_____ 3. Trash-cover Cultivating   _____ 6. Land Fertilization

A. This method of planting used in semiarid climates alternates a strip of crop with a strip of fallow land in order to control wind erosion and promote effective crop production.

B. This cultivation method rotates the planting of soil-building crops with the planting of crops that rob the soil of nutrients and organic materials.

C. This conservation measure designates stable soils as suitable for annual cultivation, while dictating that other lands be used for perennial planting, grasses and legume growing, grazing land, or forest land.

D. Inorganic chemicals are used to maintain the fertility of soil with this conservation method.

E. This cultivation method requires a farmer to follow the contours of his land and construct ditches and terraces to diminish the runoff of water.

F. This conservation method leaves a cover of natural vegetation, weeds, or crops on fields as long as possible after harvest so that the soil is not exposed to the winds and rains that cause erosion.

The Recurring Droughts of Africa: Concern for a Continent

In October 1984, BBC (British Broadcasting Corporation) demonstrated with live footage the results of a lasting drought, when it ran a program about the Korem refugee camp in north-central Ethiopia. The public was appalled. Ethiopians had been suffering a famine for four years. Malnourished children were displaying signs of brain damage and retardation. Hundreds of thousands of old and young were facing starvation. Refugees who made their way to camps like the one at Korem felt lucky if relief workers were able to provide them with a single meal every three to four days. Government agencies and volunteer groups responded to the tragedy, but were unable to prevent the deaths of 300,000 people.

Ethiopia is located on the continent of Africa in a semi-arid grassland region just below the Sahara. The Sahel belt stretches 3,000 miles from the east to the west coasts of the continent and varies from 200 to 700 miles in width. It houses 100 million people in the countries of Mauritania, Senegal, Mali, Burkina Faso, Niger, Nigeria, Chad, Sudan, and Ethiopia. The average rainfall in the Sahel is 4-8 inches a year.

Sahelians have struggled with drought conditions since the beginning of history. Ancients altered their nomadic wandering routes or moved their farms to new areas to combat dry conditions. They learned to locate water-bearing roots beneath the ground and to dig deep wells. In those days, the population of the region was sparse enough to render the effects of a drought minimal.

The effects of modern droughts in the region are dramatic. Poor land management, poverty, overpopulation, and civil wars have conspired to equate droughts with famines and famines with deaths. It is estimated that from 1968 to 1973, from 50,000 to 200,000 rural citizens and 3.5 million head of cattle died in the Sahel region due to famines. In the 1984 famine, 200,000 victims died in Mozambique alone. Two million Ethiopians starved from 1972-1990 when their country was inflicted with four major droughts. Nearly 30 African nations are plagued by hunger today.

The hope for a solution to problems associated with recurrent African droughts and famines is dim. The Sahel's soil does not recover the effects of one drought before another hits. Cow dung that was once used to enrich the soil is now used as fuel by a growing, poverty-stricken population. The pressure of the population growth forces the plowing of fallow fields, cutting of the region's forests, and cultivation of steep slopes that are susceptible to erosion. Inadequate rainfall and poor soil have forced many farmers to migrate to slums in the cities. Others have turned to the production of cash crops like cotton and cassava, which bring money but do not feed hungry mouths.

The world community has attempted to help. Emergency food supplies are delivered during the duration of African famines, but often are intercepted by warlords or corrupt politicians and used for political purposes. Agricultural experts have tried to introduce soil-conserving practices to the continent, but have met with little success due to a blatant disregard for local customs and wisdom and an ignorance of African weather patterns.

Whatever the way out of the cycle of drought and famine that afflicts the African continent, it involves an understanding of a complex set of social, political, cultural, environmental, and climatic concerns.

Definitely Dry

The Sahara and Sahel regions of northern Africa suffer drought conditions frequently. Locate the areas in another source to help you determine which of the following statements are true. Place in the blank a *T* for true and an *F* for false. The first one has been done for you.

**False** 1. The Sahara region has always been extremely dry.

_____ 2. The climate in the region just below the Sahel in West Africa can be described as tropical.

_____ 3. The effects of droughts in these regions have become worse because of poverty, increased human and livestock population, and land mismanagement.

_____ 4. In some parts of the Sahara, no rain falls for years.

_____ 5. The Sahara is primarily sand.

_____ 6. The average annual rainfall in the Sahel is 25 inches.

_____ 7. What rain does fall in the Sahel region falls primarily between June and September.

_____ 8. A large part of the population in the two regions consists of nomadic herders.

_____ 9. The Sahel is covered with grasses and shrubs.

_____ 10. The Sahara contains no major rivers.

_____ 11. The soil in the western Sahara is fertile and produces excellent crops when irrigated.

_____ 12. An oasis is a location in a desert where an underground river breaks the surface. Lush plants grow in the area of an oasis.

_____ 13. The large dunes of the Sahara are found primarily in the Libyan Desert which receives almost no rainfall and has very few oases.

_____ 14. Animal life abounds in the desert regions of the Sahara including gazelles, foxes, and hyenas.

_____ 15. Crops produced on irrigated land are the main export from the Sahara.

_____ 16. The deserts of the Sahara region are creeping into the Sahel because primitive agricultural practices have made the soil unable to adequately retain moisture.

_____ 17. A drought that affected the Sahel in the 1960s–1970s and again in the 1980s was the worst the region had seen in 150 years.

_____ 18. Peanuts are grown in the Sahel.

_____ 19. The extended droughts of the sixties, seventies, and eighties speeded up the process of desertification in the Sahel, rendering the soil unable to retain moisture.

_____ 20. Wealthy and populated Egypt is located in the Sahel region.

More Definitely Dry

The Sahara Desert is just one of many arid regions around the world. How much do you know about deserts in general? Use a science textbook to help you make the following statements true by circling the correct set of italicized words.

1. Approximately *one fourth* or *one third* of the earth's surface is arid.
2. Nearly *one fifth* or *one tenth* of the world's food supply is grown in desert regions.
3. Over *one fifth* or *one half* of the world's precious and semiprecious metals and minerals are found in desert regions.
4. The two driest places on earth are *the deserts of Peru* or *Death Valley and the Sahara Desert.*
5. About *12 percent* or *30 percent* of deserts have sand dunes.
6. The Sahara Desert is about the size of *California* or *the United States.*
7. Saharan dust storms called *harmattans* can create clouds *2,000* or *20,000* feet high that blow more than 100 million tons of dust into the Atlantic Ocean each year.
8. Winds in a desert storm can reach hurricane speeds and sandblast the paint off a car or carve strange shapes into stone. In fact, winds can move a desert *50* or *500* feet per year.
9. A desert is characterized as a region that receives an annual rainfall of less than *1* or *10* inches per year, and has an evaporation rate that exceeds its rate of precipitation.
10. Lack of moisture and *low* or *high* humidity in the atmosphere make sunlight penetrate the ground in a desert where temperatures can reach 131° F.
11. The earth contains two desert bands, one around the Tropic of Cancer and another around the Tropic of Capricorn. One of the larger northern deserts is the *Gobi* or *Arabian* desert in China.
12. The Great Sandy Deserts are located in *Argentina* or *Australia.*
13. Some desert plants are fleeting and only live for a *few hours* or *few days.*
14. *Leafy* or *Woody* desert plants survive by having either long root systems that reach deep underground water or spreading, shallow root systems that gather water from dew and occasional rain showers.
15. Desert plants have *small* or *large* leaves, succulent stems and roots that store water, and thorns to guard their stored water from animals.
16. Many desert animals reproduce only *before* or *after* winter rains.
17. Desert mammals and reptiles usually sleep *during the day* or *at night.*
18. Because so little water moves through desert soils, they are naturally *full of* or *lacking in* nutrients.
19. Crops grown in deserts are irrigated from wells and *river* or *lake* waters.
20. As much *as 15* or *35* percent of the world's arable lands are in danger of desertification, which is the process of desert encroachment.

Desert Dwellers

Few people challenge deserts the way they might mountains, yet throughout history, some adventurers have journeyed into their boundaries for reasons of adventure, commerce, or scientific discovery. Locate the following desert explorers in an encyclopedia to help you match them with their descriptions below.

IBN BATTUTA   MARCO POLO   HEINRICH BARTH   CHARLES STURT

1. This Italian pioneer of the Gobi Desert, who was once a diplomatic agent for Kublai Khan, traveled throughout the Far East extensively between 1217 and 1292. His well-written travel stories provided Europe with its first look at the geography and people of the Far East. Accurate maps were drawn following his descriptions of geography, and his vivid portrayal of places and people inspired Christopher Columbus and others to explore Asia.

   _____

2. This British explorer, who acted as secretary to the South Wales governor Ralph Darling in the early 1800s, made three trips into the interior of Australia. During one venture into the Outback, he spent six months at a single water hole when temperatures that soared to 119 degrees prevented him from proceeding. The high temperatures caused lead to fall out of his pencils, ink to dry as he attempted to write, and screws to be drawn out of the wood in his traveling trunks.

   _____

3. Between 1825 and 1880, over 200 European travelers attempted to find the ancient African city of Timbuktu, once the prosperous unofficial capital of the Sahel. Some adventurers died of fever. Others, like the Scotsman Alexander Laing who was strangled by his guide, were murdered. Most were turned back by the harsh conditions of the desert. This man, too, was given up for dead when he did not return in five years time. However, he had reached Timbuktu alive—observing, measuring, and recording details about the desert over the duration of his trip. The records he brought back to Germany provide information and maps of West African regions that remain little known today.

   _____

4. The writings of this fourteenth-century African explorer are a definitive source of history and geography of the medieval Muslim world. During 30 years of travel from Spain in the West to China in the East, this man trekked 75,000 miles. His descriptions of the Sahel area and the booming town of Timbuktu maintain that the sub-Saharan region was once a green, fertile place.

   _____

Summer Scorcher:
Hot and Dry in '88

It was a very dry year in 1988. Forty-five percent of the country suffered drought conditions during some portion of the summer. States from Texas to the Canadian border recorded less than 50% of their normal seasonal precipitation. In Minneapolis, Minnesota, no more than ¼" of rain fell during the month of June instead of the customary 4 inches. In places, the Mississippi flowed more like a stream than a river in the summer of 1988.

The year 1988 was not only a dry year, but a hot year as well. Weather stations in the midwestern and central plains states reported record high temperatures throughout the summer. Many communities endured days of 100°+ F temperatures. Both Valentine, Nebraska, and Sioux Falls, South Dakota, suffered a day at 110°F. Over 5,000 people died of heat-related illnesses during the drought, and the nation lost $40 billion in destroyed crops and drought-related business and industry expenses.

Yet the most devastating effect of the widespread 1988 drought was not felt in the cities and towns, but in the wilderness. Six million acres of American wild country burned in the scorching summer of 1988. Nearly a million of them were in Yellowstone National Park.

On July 14, 1988, Yellowstone officials were warned by the National Weather Service that the park was likely to experience hotter and drier summer conditions than it was accustomed to. A single day later, one of four minor fires in the park grew into wildfire status. In all, 11,000 acres throughout Yellowstone were covered in blazes that day. By the end of the summer, a million acres—nearly half of the park—had been touched by fire.

Reluctantly, Yellowstone officials suspended a policy of allowing fires to burn naturally, when it became clear that the entire park was in danger of being consumed in flames. More than 25,000 firefighters were recruited to arrest 249 separate fires.

Trees, wildflowers, grasses, and animals were all enveloped in blazes. Two hundred and fifty-seven elk died in Yellowstone that year along with four deer and two moose. Human lives were threatened when a firestorm approached the Old Faithful Inn, carried by 50 m.p.h. winds. Thankfully, staff and visitors were able to take refuge in the parking lot, which escaped serious damage.

On September 11, 1988, the park finally enjoyed precipitation in the form of snowfall. Although fires continued to smolder until November, without the hot, dry winds of a drought to carry them, the flames posed no threat to the park's people or wildlife any longer. The summer scorcher finally ended.

Glorious Geysers and Wonderful Wildlife

Yellowstone National Park, located in the central Rocky Mountains and expanding from northwestern Wyoming to southwestern Montana and eastern Idaho, is the oldest national park in the United States, having been established in 1872. It is famous for its geysers (including Old Faithful), rivers, hot springs, waterfalls, canyons, and wildlife.

Vacationers visit Yellowstone to camp, hike, bike, sightsee, ski, fish, boat, and picnic. They wander through museums, explore the Yellowstone volcanic caldera, and observe black bears, coyotes, and red foxes in their natural habitats.

Locate information and illustrations of Yellowstone in an encyclopedia, a Yellowstone brochure, a national park reference book, or on the Internet. Then create a Yellowstone National Park travel brochure below. The first page should include a drawing of wildlife, forests, rivers, or geysers in the park. The next page should include a map of some part of the park. The last page should list all of the activities available at the park.

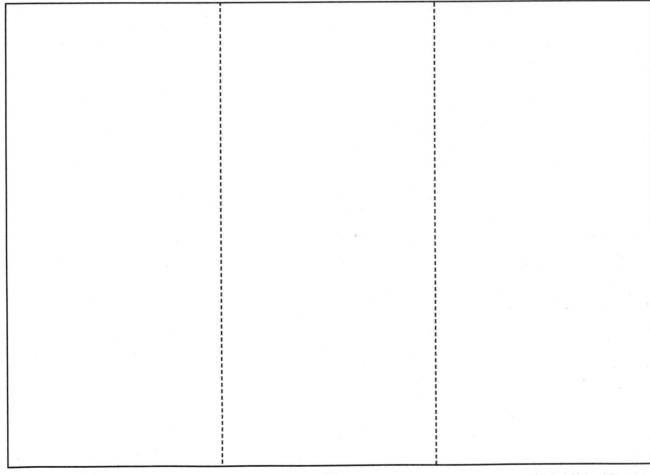

Name _____

Refraining from Fanning
the Flames

Many people live in or near wooded areas that can be affected by fast-spreading wildfires. When a wildfire threatens an area, residents should listen to battery-operated radios for reports. *If advised to evacuate, they should do so immediately.* If evacuation is not imminent, however, there are steps that can be followed to help protect a home before it is evacuated. Which of the following Red Cross fire safety tips should be applied on a regular basis, and which should be followed only when an actual wildfire threatens the area? Fill in the blank provided with the words *routine precautions* or *emergency procedures* to label the type of preparations described. The first one has been done for you.

<u>Routine Precautions</u>   1. Install a smoke alarm outside each sleeping area on each level of your home. Use the test button to check all smoke alarms once a month. Replace all batteries at least once a year.

_____   2. Close windows, doors, vents, venetian blinds, and heavy drapes. Remove lightweight curtains.

_____   3. Move flammable furniture into the center of the home away from windows and sliding glass doors. Place combustible patio furniture inside.

_____   4. Consider having fire extinguishers in your home and/or installing an automatic fire sprinkler system.

_____   5. Determine at least two ways to escape from each room in your home. Practice your escape plan at least once a year.

_____   6. Shut off gas at the meter. Turn off pilot lights. Turn off propane tanks.

_____   7. Report to your local fire department or forestry office hazardous conditions that could cause a wildfire.

_____   8. Open fireplace damper. Close fireplace screens.

_____   9. Turn on a light in each room to increase the visibility of your home in heavy smoke.

_____ 10. Regularly clean roof and gutters.

_____ 11. Inspect chimneys at least twice a year. Clean them at least once a year. Keep the dampers in good working order. Equip chimneys and stovepipe with a spark arrester that meets National Fire Protection Association Code 211 requirements.

_____ 12. Seal attic and ground vents with pre-cut plywood or commercial seals.

_____ 13. Maintain a disaster supply kit including food, water, and first-aid supplies.

_____ 14. Connect garden hose to outdoor tap. Place lawn sprinklers on roof and near above-ground fuel tanks. Wet the roof. Wet or remove shrubs within 15 feet of home.

_____ 15. Use fire-resistant materials on the roof and exterior structure of the buildings on your property.

_____ 16. Landscape your yard using fire-resistant shrubs and trees.

Natural Management of Wildfires

Prior to 1970, fires in the Yellowstone National Forest were suppressed whenever possible. Following 1970, fire management personnel at the park were instructed to let fires burn themselves out naturally unless they threatened buildings or people. The scientific community remains divided as to the effectiveness of each policy. Although some bemoan the losses experienced in 1988 because firefighters did not contain the flames initially, others suggest that the recent fire behaved much as fires that have affected the area over the centuries. Some scientists even contend that the massive fire of the late 1980s was so massive only because smaller natural fires were not permitted to run their course prior to the 1970s. Do you think wildfires should be suppressed or allowed to run their course? Justify your opinion in a single page essay below.

_____

_____

_____

_____

_____

_____

_____

_____

_____

_____

_____

_____

_____

_____

_____

_____

_____

_____

_____

_____

_____

_____

Hot Time in the Old Town Tonight

Droughts trigger fires not only in forests, but in developed areas as well. Legend has it that a cow started the great Chicago fire of 1871 when she kicked over a lantern. Yet a single barn fire would not likely have spread to an entire city had it not followed a 14-week drought in the region. Using the facts about the fire recorded below, write one of the following documents on your own paper: (A) A newspaper account of the fire

(B) A letter from a fire victim to out-of-town relatives

(C) A commemorative speech about the fire to be presented to a Chicago historical association

FACT 1: On Sunday, October 8, 1871, at 9:00 p.m., a fire broke out in a cow barn on the property of Patrick O'Leary. Although legend suggests a cow kicked over a lantern in the barn, police found no evidence to support this rumor. It is unknown how the fire did start.

FACT 2: By 1:30 a.m., Chicago's business district was in flames. Both nature and man played a role in the quick spread of the fire. A 14-week drought had parched the Midwest by October 8, 1871. Strong winds blew on the eighth and ninth. Still, the fire might have more readily been contained if so many buildings in the city were not constructed of wood.

FACT 3: Rain that began to fall around midnight on Monday, October 9, helped put out the Chicago fire. In the end, 300 people were dead and 98,500 were homeless. Property damages were estimated at $200 million as 17,450 buildings burned to the ground and 2,124 acres were destroyed.

FACT 4: The great fire left the city without water, gas, or street cars. Army personnel, city officials, relief organizations, businesses, and common citizens pulled together to keep the city functioning. Church basements and school auditoriums were set up as emergency hospitals. Railroad companies offered free tickets to hundreds of people who chose to leave the city. Freight trains transported food and clothing from other cities into Chicago for free. Common citizens organized night watches to monitor the progress of the fast-approaching flames. Friends, relatives, neighbors, and strangers all worked together to get one anothers' family members and most precious material goods to the shore of Lake Michigan, another place of safety.

FACT 5: Numerous government and commercial buildings were burned to the ground in the flames of the Chicago fire. Only one wholesale warehouse stood when the flames subsided. The courthouse, customs house, post office, and numerous hotels, theaters, museums, opera houses, banks, and businesses were destroyed along with their records, art collections, and goods.

FACT 6: Chicago was quickly rebuilt. By 1875 it was a thriving city again. Buildings were constructed under stricter fire code regulations, and the site of the O'Leary cow barn was transformed into the Chicago Fire Academy.

Water in the West:
Engineering the Colorado River

A six-year drought in California beginning in the mid-1980s forced average citizens and government officials alike to reexamine the historical role of water in the West. Prior to the gold rush era, the sparsely populated western coast of America was little disturbed by the desert and drought conditions that existed in the region. Native Americans knew how to locate water-bearing roots and underground water sources. And they were not tied to the land, so an occasional dry spell became only a nuisance to a tribe that pulled up stakes and relocated periodically.

Then in the late 1800s and early 1900s the population of California exploded. William Mulholland, superintendent of the Los Angeles water system, attempted to convince city residents to conserve water, when he discovered that the Los Angeles River was being sucked dry. Proving unsuccessful at persuading residents to conserve, he sought out a new source of water for Los Angeles. Over the course of 12 years, his agents purchased water rights to the Owens River and built a 233-mile aqueduct across the Mojave Desert to deliver its waters to Los Angeles. When the Owens River dried up as well, Mulholland's predecessors harnessed water from the Colorado River, some 300 miles east of the city.

Los Angeles was not the only drought-prone, semi-arid community in the west to look to that great river for its abundant waters. By the 1960s the Colorado had become the most controlled and over-allocated river in the history of the world. Numerous dams and diversions engineered the river's flow so completely, that by 1969, it no longer reached the Pacific Ocean except in especially wet years.

The construction of the Colorado River's famous Hoover Dam encouraged the creation of countless other flood control, hydroelectric, and irrigation systems throughout the West. Fifty-five dams were built on the Columbia River alone. A computer-monitored aqueduct in Arizona was constructed across 300 miles of desert. Reservoirs which displaced wildlife and upset environmental balances were erected in previously undisturbed forests.

Still, such engineering marvels proved insufficient in providing for the agricultural, commercial, and residential needs of communities in the desert and drought-prone regions of the West. The enormous amount of water used by California's agricultural Central Valley—a naturally semi-arid region—began to create artificial droughts in the valley during seasons that received normal precipitation. Today, when the region gets hit with a naturally occurring dry spell on top of the human-induced ones, residents feel the effects. Temporary ordinances prohibit lawn watering and car washing. Government agencies promote the use of low-capacity flushing toilets and water-conserving shower heads. "Water patrols" monitor corporate water usage.

These conservation measures are tolerable compared with those suffered by other regions of the world. The Middle East depends on desalinization plants, which remove salt from sea water. China is considering the construction of the world's largest dam, which would displace over one million people and flood a canyon as large as our Grand Canyon. Residents in Mexico City pay up to 25% of their income to purchase water that is brought into their community by truck. For the American West, the 1980's six-year drought was a stark warning that water use and societal growth are on a collision course. The region is reconsidering water issues and rewriting water regulations, keeping in mind both human and environmental concerns.

Drip, Drop, Drought

The Colorado River provides water to so many communities that it is dry before it reaches the Pacific Ocean. Huge western cities, including Los Angeles and Phoenix, which were developed in desert environments, depend on the river maintaining a certain water level achieved by annual runoff. So, when the West suffers a dry season, its citizens have learned to conserve.

Decide which of the following water conservation methods are employed only during droughts and which are encouraged year round. Write *year round* or *during droughts* in the blank before each water conservation approach. The first one has been done for you.

__During Droughts__ 1. The water hoses and car washes at gas stations are shut off.

_____ 2. Waste water is recycled and used to water golf courses and public lands.

_____ 3. Water prices are raised so that residents of dry regions will be less inclined to wash cars, water lawns, or overuse water.

_____ 4. Farming techniques are developed that leave more moisture in the ground.

_____ 5. Water is offered in restaurants only upon request.

_____ 6. Residential districts are restricted in the number of days per week they are permitted to water their lawns, or lawn watering is prohibited altogether.

_____ 7. Cities employ "water patrols" to ensure city ordinances concerning water conservation are observed.

_____ 8. Residents are encouraged to fix leaky faucets. Cities repair leaky pipes.

_____ 9. Plants are irrigated only when they wilt.

_____ 10. Scientists experiment with desalting ocean waters, cloud-seeding, and utilizing the water contained in ice caps.

_____ 11. Residents of semi-arid communities are encouraged to install low-capacity flushing toilets and water-conserving shower heads.

_____ 12. A region's residents are asked to reuse dishwater to wash clothes, vegetable-washing water to water plants, and/or washing machine water to mop floors, flush toilets, or wash cars.

_____ 13. Citizens are encouraged to wash only full loads of clothes in washing machines and full loads of dishes in dishwashers.

_____ 14. Residents are encouraged to use automatic timers or drip irrigation in place of sprinkler lawn-watering systems.

_____ 15. Residents are encouraged to install a hose head with a squeeze handle sprayer for use when washing cars or watering plants so that water does not continue to flow when not in use.

Rainmakers

Humankind has devised many plans for providing arid lands and thirsty people with fresh water. Schemes have included seeding clouds to induce rainfall, rerouting water by means of huge dams and long aqueducts, desalting the waters of seas and oceans, and moving enormous blocks of glacier ice to drought-prone regions. Formulate your own plan for providing dry regions with fresh water. Describe your plan, using words and drawings below.

Dams and Ditches

Historians studying water issues describe America's past decision-making process about water as assessing the needs of the people and building the means of providing for them. Today lawmakers, environmentalists, and residents of drought-prone regions are not so certain this was a wise approach. Deltas have been transformed into dried-out salt flats, due to the damming of waters upstream. Aquifers that took centuries to fill are being depleted in decades. Lakes, wetlands, and surface streams are shrinking due to water diversions.

Teaching the world's citizens to approach water in a new way may be the last hope we have of meeting commercial, agricultural, and residential needs for fresh water supplies. On your own paper, write a two- to five-minute speech convincing your classmates to conserve water. You may wish to include some of the facts that follow.

- Most of the world's inhabitants do not have access to a reliable, fresh supply of water.
- Only 7% of the planet's water is fresh water; 2.5% of that is located in deep, underground aquifers and 2% is frozen in ice caps.
- Agriculture uses the most water in the United States.
- It requires 1,000 gallons of water to grow and process one pound of food.
- It requires 40,000 gallons of water to produce the steel necessary to build one automobile.
- A running garden hose wastes 10 gallons of water per minute.
- Sixty percent of the water used to water your lawn during warm months is lost to evaporation.
- A leaky faucet can waste 3,000 gallons of water a year.
- An average toilet uses 6 gallons of water every time it flushes as opposed to the 1.6 gallons used by low-level capacity models.
- An average kitchen or bathroom faucet puts out 4 gallons of water per minute.
- Water pollution limits the amount of available fresh water in industrialized nations.
- The average consumption rate of water in the United States ranges from 100–250 gallons per person per day.
- Water makes up 50%–90% of the weight of all living organisms.
- In 1962 Buckeye, Arizona, became the world's first town to provide for all of its water needs by means of a water desalinization plant.
- Desalting ocean water costs about $1 per 1,000 gallons as opposed to the $.05–$.30 residents are assessed for 1,000 gallons of water provided by wells and reservoirs.

Devastating Floods

What Is a Flood?
Why Do Floods Occur?

A flood is a great flowing of water over land that is normally dry. A coastal flood occurs in a beach area lining an ocean or sea; a river flood occurs in a floodplain region—a flat plain area along the course of a stream or river; and a flash flood occurs most frequently in mountainous areas or desert regions.

Coastal floods result from one of a number of occurrences. Sometimes an exceptionally high tide combines with a moderate storm to inundate the land with water. On other occasions, tsunamis caused by surface-level or underwater earthquakes or volcanoes cause ocean waters to rise significantly and flood coastal regions. Frequently, hurricanes and tropical storms cause coastal flooding.

River flooding occurs when soil and vegetation in a region cannot hold any more moisture and the resulting runoff is too much to be contained by stream channels, ponds, lakes, or reservoirs. Heavy rains and/or melting snows periodically cause natural river rising, but man is responsible for some river floods. Deforestation and land paving reduce the soil's ability to absorb rainfall. Landfills and construction projects constrict the natural flow of runoff and river waters. Man-made dams designed to control waters sometimes cause flooding when they collapse due to poor construction, poor location, old age, or the movements of an earthquake or landslide.

Heavy rains and/or melting snows cause short-lived flash floods to occur with little warning in mountainous regions where runoff water joins forces with overflowing streams, or in desert areas where large amounts of moisture cannot be contained in the soil.

Why Are Floods Dangerous?

Floods are the most frequently occurring of all natural disasters, and they cause 40% of all deaths caused by natural disasters. In the United States alone, an average of 200 people die each year in floods. In Bangladesh, where monsoon rains fall annually, floods frequently drown more than half of the nation.

Floods not only threaten human lives. Rapid runoff increases the speed of soil and deposits sediment downstream that raises river beds, constricts stream flows, and changes the course of rivers. High flood waters delay traffic, ruin crops, destroy wildlife habitats, and damage bridges, sewer systems, homes, and other structures. In the United States, property losses related to flood damage have exceeded $4 billion in some years.

Can Floods Be Predicted or Prevented?

Although flash floods occur with little or no warning, many floods can be predicted by scientists and meteorologists who monitor weather patterns and study the workings of the hydrologic cycle.

Coastal flooding cannot be effectively prevented, but structural and nonstructural controls prevent much river flooding. Structural controls include levees that raise the banks of a river, floodways that divert flood waters, and channel straightening which increases the rate of flow of flood water. Reforestation of watersheds also lessens soil erosion, while dams and reservoirs help store excessive runoff. Nonstructural controls refer to legislative efforts to regulate the use of rivers and floodplains and promote soil conservation and land management procedures.

Name _____

Flood Facts

Indicate which of the following statements about floods are true and which are false in the spaces provided.

_____ 1. Electrocution is the number one cause of deaths during floods.

_____ 2. During floods, more people drown in their homes than anywhere else.

_____ 3. Food, cosmetics, and medicines that have been touched by flood waters should be discarded because flood waters pick up sewage and chemicals from farms, factories, and roads along the way.

_____ 4. More than half of the world's population lives near oceans or rivers.

_____ 5. Only the Gobi desert and parts of the Sahara are free from the risk of flooding.

_____ 6. A levee built on the banks of the Yellow River by ancient Chinese was responsible for saving locals from rising water levels on the river 4,000 years later during an 1887 storm.

_____ 7. Modern levees, which raise the banks of a river, make necessary repeated dredging of the affected river so that deposits do not raise the river bed.

_____ 8. Ice or debris can block the flow of a river and cause a flood upstream, or a flash flood downstream, when it becomes dislodged.

_____ 9. Flood waters typically move at a very slow pace.

_____ 10. A car can float in only two feet of water.

_____ 11. Runoff from paved areas is two to six times greater than that from natural terrain.

_____ 12. Nearly a hundred river forecasting centers around the United States collaborate to forecast floods.

_____ 13. There are over 3 million miles of stream and river in the United States.

_____ 14. A flood watch indicates that a flood is possible in a given region.

_____ 15. Many floods occur when it is not raining.

_____ 16. Farmers, fishermen, and dam operators are among the many people who rely on the reports of flood forecasters.

_____ 17. A good rule of thumb suggests that if flood waters are higher than your knees, do not try to wade through them.

_____ 18. Flood waters traveling at 8 miles per hour exert 264 pounds of force per square foot.

_____ 19. An acre foot is a measure of flood water indicating the amount of water needed to cover one acre of land with one yard of water.

_____ 20. The rich soils that lure farmers to settle in floodplain regions gained their richness from deposits left from past floods.

_____ 21. Less than one percent of U.S. land is prone to flooding.

_____ 22. Many U.S. cities were developed near rivers because they provided the communities with much-needed water supplies.

_____ 23. One thousand communities in the United States face occasional flooding problems.

Name _____

Drying Out

Cleaning up after a flood that has affected your home will take a long time. Everything flood waters (which have been contaminated by chemicals and sewage along the way) have touched will need to be washed, disinfected, and dried out. Match the cleaning procedures below with the areas that need to be cleaned. The first one has been done for you. (Cleaning tips have been provided by the American Red Cross.)

Walls	Windows	Furniture	Clothing and Linens
Kitchen Items	Papers and Books	The Yard	Appliances
The Lawn	Computer Disks	Food	

_____Walls_____ 1. Begin cleaning at the bottom where the worst flood damage has occurred. If wallboards or plaster require removal, wash and disinfect studs and sills before replacing the boards or plaster.

_____ 2. Professionally clean items that have a label indicating they hold an electric charge even when unplugged. You may clean many other items yourself. Unplug, disassemble, hose thoroughly, wash and disinfect, dry with blow dryer, and reassemble.

_____ 3. If these were taped shut before the storm, remove tape as soon as possible since sunlight will bake the adhesive into the glass. Use tar remover, nail polish remover, or razor blades to help you accomplish the task.

_____ 4. Do not use the washing machine until you know that your water is safe enough to drink and your sewer lines are working. Run the machine through one cycle with hot water and disinfectant before use.

_____ 5. Rinse with clear water and place in a plastic bag in the refrigerator until you can get the items to a professional drying center.

_____ 6. Do not force open swollen wooden drawers. They should open when they dry out. Remove the backs of items to let air circulate. Wood alcohol and turpentine will remove white mildew spots on wood. Most upholstered items will need to be thrown out.

_____ 7. Wash by hand in a disinfectant. Air dry. Plastic and porous items which probably absorbed contaminated flood waters will need to be thrown out.

_____ 8. Hose off the salt water. Replace grass that has been under one inch of mud or more or has come in contact with grass-killing chemicals.

_____ 9. Rinse and freeze until you have time to restore. Then thaw and dry out quickly with a blow drier. Photocopy important records after drying since substances in the flood waters may make them deteriorate.

_____10. Throw out any that has been touched by flood waters—even those stored in cans, bottles, and jars.

_____11. Drain or remove standing water as it can become a breeding ground for mosquitoes. Clean ditches, gutters, and drains so they can carry storm water away. Dump water out of barrels, old tires, and cans.

100% Chance of Rain

Predicting floods is challenging work because hydrologists need to monitor not only rainfall, but snow melt, soil moisture content, and the amount of water in streams as well as in the atmosphere. Match the goals of flood predicting on the left with the challenges they present on the right. Notice that some goals present more than one challenge.

Goal

_____1. Determine the amount of water that the soil in a region can absorb.

_____2. Monitor the amount of water in streams and rivers so it can be determined how much more water they can hold.

_____3. Monitor the amount of water being yielded by melting snow.

_____4. Determine the amount of water in the atmosphere to help forecast precipitation.

_____5. Document the amount of rainfall in a given region.

_____6. Measure the rate at which runoff waters reach streams and rivers.

Challenge

A. The rate of evaporation varies with changes in wind, temperature, and humidity.

B. Different types of soil absorb different amounts of water.

C. Fast-flowing flood waters alter streambeds, changing the rate at which water moves out of rivers and streams and into lakes, reservoirs, and oceans.

D. The amount of water soil can absorb depends on the amount of water the soil is already holding.

E. The moisture content of snow varies from region to region and from snowfall to snowfall.

F. The amount of rain that falls in one spot where a gauge is located is never identical to the amount that falls even one mile away.

G. The rate at which snow melts depends on many factors, such as wind, temperature, snowpack, and sunlight.

H. The rate of runoff varies with different terrains and the presence of man-made structures and paved roads.

I. Although weather radar gives a general picture of where rain has fallen, it does not yield detailed information about the amount of precipitation a region has received.

China's Yellow River:
The Ungovernable

In the Great Plains of Northern China lies the world's fourth largest river and the earth's most deadly natural resource. The Yellow River, nicknamed the *Ungovernable* or *China's Great Sorrow,* has topped its banks 1,500 times in the past 3,500 years. In so doing, it has changed its course 26 times, covering crops and houses in silt and debris and claiming the lives of millions of peasant farmers.

The Yellow River is named for the color of the silt it carries and deposits in the sea and on its floodplains. A remarkable amount of sand from the Gobi Desert makes its way to the Yellow River via numerous tributaries. In some places, silt has elevated the bed of the river so much that the water flows 13–26 feet above the surrounding countryside. In other places 46% of the river's weight is made up of dirt. When the banks overflow, the Yellow River produces floodwaters that can be composed of as much as 70% sand.

The history of the Yellow River is steeped in flood stories. Legends suggest that 23 centuries before the birth of Christ, the region suffered a 13-year flood. Folklore contends that a man named Yu tamed the river for 1,600 years at one point in history by mandating frequent river dredging and the maintenance of numerous diversion canals. Historians write of deliberate dike-breaking during times of war, as well as interesting attempts at flood prevention including the sacrificing of young women to the river.

Still, 70 million farmers choose to cultivate the fertile silt plains that line the banks of the Yellow River. Some live in caves below their fields. Others build huts on terraced hillsides. All work together to plug holes, add height to dikes, create silt-settling ponds, and maintain dams and reservoirs in an attempt to curtail the river's flooding.

In 1887 flooding would not be contained. Although exact statistics are not available, it has been estimated that 2.5 million people died of drowning, starvation, or disease in China's Great Plains that year. Sometime in October of that year, a long stretch of dikes gave way to the forces of swift-flowing silt and water, and an undetermined number of people were swept away in flowing mud. Uncontained by dams, the floodwaters rushed through 1,500 towns and villages to cover an area roughly the size of Lake Ontario. Survivors reportedly clung to rooftops, tree branches, terraced hillsides, and floating debris, but their troubles were not over.

When the waters finally receded, ten feet of silt lay atop the region's buildings, as well as its wheat, millet, and potato crops. Flood victims had no food, no clothing, and no homes. Missionaries rowed up and down the now-quieted river throwing bread to the masses here and there, but thousands died of starvation. Another half million Great Plains' residents died of cholera because they lacked clean drinking water.

On January 6, 1888, work on dike repairs began again. Stones were transported for miles in ox-driven carts, and thousands of tons of earth were carried one wheelbarrow load at a time to the dike's rupture. In nine months' time the dike was holding back the river again. Today, pumps, reservoirs, dikes, stream-flow gauging stations, computers, and hydrologists all work together to harness the Yellow River. Hydrologists claim that they have governed the ungovernable. Although they may not have completely controlled the Yellow River, they can at least warn the region's residents of conditions that require their immediate evacuation so that the death toll due to Yellow River flooding never has to reach 2.5 million again.

Look Out Below!

Much of the destruction that accompanies Yellow River flooding episodes is caused not by water, but by mud. Mudslides are natural, recurring forces of nature that cause billions of dollars in damages and countless deaths around the globe each year. Practice your reading comprehension skills by using your own paper to answer the questions below based on the following mudslide facts.

1. Deforestation and the development of landslide-prone regions increases the occurrence of mudslides.
2. Mudslides can be triggered by heavy thunderstorms, flash floods, regular floods, earthquakes, or volcanoes.
3. In the United States, landslides cause from 25 to 50 deaths and $1.5 billion worth of damages each year.
4. The west coast of the American continent is one of the most landslide-prone regions in the world.
5. In 1985 mudflows in Colombia killed 20,000 people.
6. Much of the death and destruction during Hurricane Mitch in Central America in November 1998 was caused by mudslides.
7. Landslide-prone regions are easy to define by their steep banks and long-term mudflow history, but people often ignore the signs and build in these areas because they offer great views of oceans or rich farming soil.
8. Conditions must be perfect to produce mudslides. Water must be introduced into the soil at perfectly timed intervals and in just the right amounts.
9. If a mudslide has affected a hillside once, it will affect it again. But since many years may pass between the two occurrences, regional residents may "forget" that their hillsides are vulnerable to slides.
10. In 1982 the San Francisco area was reminded that it was a slide-prone region when a severe storm dumped 24 inches of rain on the Bay Area and caused 18,000 different mudslides in ten counties.
11. Mudslide controls include building debris dams and retaining structures, grading slopes, and implementing landslide-warning systems, based on precipitation and ground-water absorption levels.
12. Geomorphologists have trouble studying mudslides because the behavior of mud is not exactly like that of a liquid or that of a solid. Mudslides also occur unpredictably and are over so quickly that they do not lend themselves to direct study.

Questions
1. What triggers mudslides? What conditions make mudslides more likely to occur?
2. Are the words *mudslide, mudflow,* and *landslide* used interchangeably in the information above?
3. Why is it difficult to study mudslides?
4. Why do people build homes in landslide-prone areas?
5. What mudslide controls are utilized in landslide-prone regions today?
6. What statistics in the information above validate the statement that the American west coast is highly susceptible to mudslides?

The Yangtze: The Yellow River's Southern Sister

China's Yangtze River (also known as the Chang Jiang) is the largest river in China. Located in the Himalayan Plateau, its banks are home to 250 million people. The Yangtze is both a blessing and a curse to the Chinese people. About 70% of China's rice is produced in the river's basin regions. The Yangtze and its tributaries provide a transportation system that is more traveled than the total of all other rivers in China. If developed, a hydroelectric system on the river could provide as much as 40% of China's necessary power.

On the negative side, the Yangtze River averages a major flood every ten years. In 1931, when the river overflowed and mud covered the basin's crops, 3.7 million people drowned or starved. In 1954 another 30,000 fell victim to the river's forces. It required three million peasants and soldiers to rebuild the dam following the flood that year. In one city, 10,000 people stood hand-in-hand in waist-deep water to form a human dike until their places could be covered with sandbag stacks. In 1991 another 1,000 people died as a result of Yangtze River flooding.

Yet flooding in the area, like the river itself, has both negative and positive consequences. While major floods kill people and livestock and destroy crops and property, frequent minor floods provide the region with the rich, fertile soil used to produce so much of the nation's rice. Most natural disasters, in fact, have both an up and a down side. Write the negative and positive consequences of the natural disasters listed below. You do not need to use complete sentences.

	Negative Consequences	Positive Consequences
1. Fires	_____	_____
	_____	_____
2. Volcanoes	_____	_____
	_____	_____
3. Floods	_____	_____
	_____	_____
4. Earthquakes	_____	_____
	_____	_____
5. Tornadoes	_____	_____
	_____	_____
6. Hurricanes	_____	_____
	_____	_____

The Effects of El Niño

Name _____

Every three to seven years, the sea surface of the southeastern tropical Pacific warms to an unusually high temperature. Since ocean temperatures substantially affect the earth's weather, man and nature feel the effects of these El Niños. Historians suggest, in fact, that many flooding episodes and other weather events throughout history have been caused by El Niño's warming of ocean waters. What do you know about El Niños? Decide which of the following statements are true and which are false.

_____ 1. A Peruvian fisherman named the El Niño effect after the Christ Child because El Niños affect weather patterns from around Christmas until near Easter time.

_____ 2. During the 1997–1998 El Niño, coastal flooding increased in California, Oregon, and Washington.

_____ 3. El Niños increase easterly winds blowing across the tropical Pacific.

_____ 4. El Niños commonly increase hurricane activity in the North Atlantic.

_____ 5. The abnormal ocean temperature warming of an El Niño typically occurs during the months of December through March.

_____ 6. During the 1997–1998 El Niño, southern Alaska experienced warmer and wetter conditions than normal.

_____ 7. During a 1982–1983 El Niño, the French Polynesia suffered six major typhoons.

_____ 8. The 1982–1983 hurricane season in the Atlantic experienced only two storms—the fewest it had experienced in a single season in 50 years.

_____ 9. Weaker than normal trade winds alert meteorologists to a possible El Niño season.

_____ 10. A 1972–1973 El Niño ruined fishing in Peru by turning the normally deep, cold, nutrient-rich waters of the western Pacific into warm, shallow waters that did not support anchovy life.

_____ 11. Because expected monsoon rains fell before they reached the continent, the 1972–1973 El Niño caused a severe drought in India.

_____ 12. Because the earth's weather patterns are not significantly tied together, El Niños do not affect the entire globe.

_____ 13. During 1982 and 1983, eastern Australia, southern Africa, and Indonesia suffered severe droughts due to the effects of an El Niño.

_____ 14. Fish that live in cold waters and birds that eat them usually survive the warm waters of an El Niño.

_____ 15. The continent that suffers the most economic hardships from El Niño is South America.

_____ 16. The most severe El Niño of the twentieth century occurred in 1997–1998.

The Great Potato Famine

Floods and droughts are not the only natural disasters that cause mass starvation, disease, and economic disaster. From 1846 through 1850, a blight or fungus caused acre after acre of potatoes in Ireland to rot. Farmers who relied on the crops to pay their bills were forced off their farms. Hundreds of thousands of peasants who attempted to emigrate to America died on overcrowded boats soon known as "coffin ships." Peasants who ate the blighted potatoes were struck with cholera and typhus. Men, women, and children starved to death by the millions.

How much do you know about the plant that caused so much trouble? Write *true* or *false* in the spaces provided beside the potato trivia below.

_____ 1. Potatoes grow on a potato plant when the plant's white or bluish-purple blossoms turn into a seedball and then into a full grown potato.

_____ 2. The average American eats about 124 pounds of potatoes each year.

_____ 3. To keep potatoes for a long period of time, store them in the refrigerator.

_____ 4. A single potato provides about 100% of the recommended daily requirement of dietary fiber in an adult diet.

_____ 5. The potato is a fat-free food.

_____ 6. Idaho provides the United States with the majority of its potatoes.

_____ 7. One medium potato contains about 420 calories.

_____ 8. Potatoes are grown in about 125 countries around the world.

_____ 9. The potato is of the same plant family as tobacco or tomatoes.

_____ 10. The french fry was first introduced to Americans by Ben Franklin after he returned from one of his state visits to France.

_____ 11. Potato production is increasing at a rate second only to that of corn worldwide.

_____ 12. Potatoes are the fourth most important food crop in the world behind wheat, rice, and maize.

_____ 13. Potatoes originated in Ireland.

_____ 14. The greatest producer of potatoes today is Russia.

_____ 15. The potato famine in Ireland resulted in a population decrease in Ireland from 8 million to 5 million citizens.

Johnstown, Pennsylvania:
Death of a Dam

The 30,000 residents of Johnstown, Pennsylvania, never wanted a dam and reservoir built 15 miles to their northeast. The mountain-valley community already had three rivers merge inside its borders, which subjected its people to periodic flooding. An enormous chamber of water sitting 450 feet higher than the city would create an additional threat Johnstown did not need. However, the Pennsylvania state government felt differently. A reserve supply of water would ensure that even during dry spells the three rivers that merged in Johnstown would have enough water to float ships full of industrial goods through the Allegheny Mountains.

So the reservoir was dug and the dam was built—slowly. By the time the project was completed 13 years later in 1853, a railway ran through Johnstown, and the rivers were no longer needed to transport goods. Upon its christening, the South Fork Dam was already obsolete.

For 25 years, the dam and reservoir sat above the city, ill-maintained and useless, until 1879 when a private citizen, Benjamin F. Ruff, bought the enormous water chamber for $2,000. He named the reservoir Lake Conemaugh and set about transforming it. First, he patched up weak spots in the earthen dam with mud and straw because it was cheaper than thorough repairs. Then, he removed five cast-iron pipes that were used to discharge water from the reservoir into the rivers below. Next, he lowered the walls of the reservoir to make space for a road. Finally, he covered the dam's spillway with wire mesh and logs so that fish would not swim out of Lake Conemaugh. In the end, Ruff built cabins and a clubhouse around the water's edge and enticed 100 wealthy businessmen to pay $2,000 each for rights to vacation at the exclusive South Fork Fishing and Hunting Club.

Johnstown's residents were concerned about Ruff's "reservoir improvements." One man hired an engineer to inspect the dam. The engineer's report was dismal. Without a clear spillway and the cast-iron pipes Ruff removed, a heavy rain could cause the reservoir to overflow. Johnstown residents sent a letter stating their concerns to Mr. Ruff, and Mr. Ruff responded: "You and your people are in no danger from our enterprise."

Ten years later, the "no danger" became a catastrophe. Beginning on May 30, 1889, a band of thunderstorms drenched west central Pennsylvania with seven inches of rain. On Friday morning, May 31, the waters of the Little Conemaugh River flowed over her banks and into Johnstown's factories, stores, and homes. The worst was yet to come. Other swollen rivers that fed into Lake Conemaugh pushed 75,000 gallons of water per second into the reservoir. Trench diggers attempted to clear the wire-meshed spillway of soggy debris. Others threw shovel-loads of dirt atop the edges of the dam to raise it. Their efforts were in vain. At 3:10 p.m. the South Fork Dam burst. The village of South Fork was wiped out as a wall of mud and water made its way down to Johnstown. Oil lamps overturned, a railroad car full of lime reacted with the water of the flood, and tons of wood and debris bobbing in the water ignited in flames. People who rode the waves on pieces of plywood or tree branches burned alive. By June 1, 1889, Johnstown, Pennsylvania, had been wiped off the map along with 2,209 of its residents by the waters of a reservoir that should not have been built.

Placing the Blame:
Man or Nature?

1. What human actions contributed to the 1889 collapse of the South Fork Dam?

   _____

   _____

   _____

   _____

2. What forces of nature contributed to the 1889 collapse of the South Fork Dam?

   _____

   _____

   _____

3. Write the headline of a newspaper article describing the disaster in a few direct words:

   _____

4. Choose one of the true accounts outlined below to write a complete newspaper article about (use your own paper):

   A. A man and wife on their honeymoon sit inside a railroad passenger car when the floodwaters hit. They climb atop the car to safety until it is swept out from under them in the water's strong current. Next, they ride on a small raft with a couple dozen other survivors who have mangled limbs and bruised bodies. When the raft heads for the molten metal of a destroyed steel factory, the couple jumps the raft and clings to floating debris until they are rescued by a man who swims from dry land to save them.

   B. Thousands of flood victims floated atop the debris of downed trees, telegraph poles, houses, stores, factories, railroad tracks, and railway cars until the enormous jumble smacked into the stone bridge at the center of town. Hundreds of people climbed onto the bridge for safety while hundreds of others, entangled in debris, burned to death when the fires started.

   C. A father of seven is swallowed up by a wall of water and debris as he attempts to run home from work. His wife sits atop the family's home with her seven children and watches in horror as each child slips under the water one after another. By the time she is rescued from her rooftop she is the only surviving member of her family.

   D. From a railroad lookout, two railway workers see the roaring waters from the reservoir rushing toward them. They run to their train, attempt to wake two sleeping brakemen in the caboose who do not awaken. With no time to spare, the workers awaken and detach the engine from the rest of the train and steer it down the track as fast as they can just ahead of the floodwaters.

Natural Weather Forecasters

Human beings are not the only ones who can predict a rainstorm like the one that broke the South Fork Dam. Plants and animals sense atmospheric changes, too. Match the following weather sayings with the reasons they often hold true. The first one has been done for you.

__B__ 1. Birds flying low,
expect rain and a blow.

____ 2. If garden spiders forsake their webs,
it indicates rain.

____ 3. Bees never get caught in the rain.

____ 4. If ants their walls do frequent build,
Rain will from the clouds be spilled.

____ 5. The gnats bite and I scratch in vain
Because they know it is going to rain.

____ 6. When leaves show their undersides
Be very sure that rain betides.

____ 7. Seaweed dry, sunny sky.
Seaweed wet, rain you'll get.

____ 8. Flowers smell best just before a rain.

____ 9. Knots get tighter before a rain.

____ 10. When the milkweed closes its pod,
expect rain.

____ 11. Frogs croaking in the lagoon
means that rain will come real soon.

____ 12. Mushrooms and toadstools are
plentiful before rain.

A. Ice crystals in clouds destroy the polarization of sunlight, making it difficult for bees to navigate, so they stay close to the hive in wet weather.

B. Low barometric pressure, which indicates precipitation, makes flying low in the sky easier than flying higher for birds.

C. Leaves curl and turn over on their branches before a rain.

D. Mushroom growth requires high humidity.

E. Insects fly lower and bite more in lowering pressure and rising humidity.

F. Plants sense moisture in the air and either close for protection or open to gather more rain water.

G. Water molecules help aromatic molecules bind better to the moisture in your nose.

H. When spider web threads absorb moisture, they break.

I. Ants reinforce their nests and cover their entrances before a rain.

J. Cold-blooded, aquatic animals require warm, moist conditions to be active.

K. Rope made of plant fibers expands when moisture fills its cellulose fibers.

L. Seaweed and moss absorb moisture.

Worldwide Flooding

Based on the names of rivers and towns mentioned in the following accounts of historic floods, match each disaster with its location.

Location of Flood

Northwestern Europe	Bangladesh	South Dakota	Missouri	Colombia	Italy
Mid-Atlantic States	Ohio	California	Paraguay	India	Georgia

_____ 1. In May 1993 the entire capital city of Dhaka stood under water when rivers overflowed their banks and claimed 200 lives.

_____ 2. This 1972 Rapid City flash flood lasted only two hours, but killed 236 people. When a thunderstorm stalled and dumped 15 inches of rain into the Rapid River, its waters rushed to the Canyon Lake Dam. Debris blocked the dam's spillway and the dam failed, pouring its contents into the streets of Rapid City.

_____ 3. Hundreds of villages in this country and in Brazil and Argentina were covered in water after two weeks of heavy rains caused the Paraguay and two other rivers to overflow.

_____ 4. This Kansas City flash flood of 1977 occurred as a result of two separate heavy storms hitting the same area during a 36-hour period.

_____ 5. In June 1972 torrential rains from Virginia to New York caused flooding that destroyed property and killed 118 people.

_____ 6. This 1977 flash flood, which destroyed the campus of Taccoa Falls, occurred when a rain-weakened dam gave way above Taccoa.

_____ 7. This area flooded in the beginning months of 1995 when rains caused the Rhine river to overflow along with other major rivers of the region.

_____ 8. Rains and mudslides caused $80 billion of damage in Los Angeles in 1978.

_____ 9. The death and destruction caused by this 1990 flood occurred when heavy rainfall on already saturated ground caused waters from the tributaries of the river to race into the river until it overflowed.

_____ 10. Coffee, banana, and cane crops were destroyed by floodwaters and mudslides when the Taparto River flowed over its banks.

_____ 11. Annual monsoon rains bring flooding to many cities in this nation, especially those located near the Ganges River.

_____ 12. When the Arno River overflowed into the streets of Florence in 1966, many famous Renaissance landmarks were damaged.

Man and the Mississippi:
An Endless Battle for Control

From a shallow lake in northern Minnesota emerges a small stream that grows substantially as it meanders southward for 2,348 miles to the Gulf of Mexico. The longest river in North America touches ten states and collects water from 100,000 streams in 31 states and two Canadian provinces. For centuries man has contended with the unruly behaviors of the waters of the Mississippi.

Native Americans who built homes on the Mississippi floodplain constructed them on high ground or on enormous man-made mounds. They understood the power of the river. The Europeans who came later did not. The French built New Orleans directly in the path of periodically occurring floodwaters, and towns up and down the river followed suit. They liked the fertile soil of the plains and depended on the river to transport cotton and manufactured goods from town to town. Unfortunately, they did not consider the river's natural, routine flooding a potential problem.

Natives warned them that the waters of the Mississippi rose higher than her banks about once every seven years. Europeans acknowledged the warning and built higher banks, or levees. The levees proved insufficient. Ground animals dug holes through the banks, crayfish whittled out homes in the mud, and gushing waters broke through weak spots in the walls of the levees continuously. Laws were passed, maintenance work was completed, but still on April 20, 1927 (in the middle of a record-breaking spring season of rains through the central United States), a levee near Memphis, Tennessee, crumbled. A seven-foot wall of water struck shore with great force. Men who had been carrying sandbags to the weakening levee's edge were swept to their deaths by the massive surge of water. Survivors were stranded on bridges and ancient Native American mounds for days until rescue workers could reach them.

Still the high waters of the Mississippi continued to exert their force. One hundred and nineteen other levees broke along the river's banks. Tributaries backed up and flooded. Sixteen-and-a-half million acres of previously dry ground in seven states lay under muddy waters that stood 18 feet deep in some places. In the end, more than 300 people died and 650,000 were displaced from their homes in the 1927 flood. Twenty-six thousand square miles of land was touched by the river, which flowed 80 miles wide in some places. Damage estimates ran as high as $230 million.

Thankfully, the U.S. government got the message: levees alone cannot contain the waters of the Mississippi. The Flood Control Act of 1928 lifted the local burden of flood control from the shoulders of towns along the banks of the Mississippi. Rejecting a widely held belief that levees were the best defense against flooding, the act funded new projects. Reservoirs and spillways were built. Artificial cutoffs were dug, and trees along the river's edge were replanted. Continuous dredging, digging, building, and research make the Mississippi River the most engineered waterway in the world.

Still the Mississippi challenges man to a contest of wills. Just as it has done countless times in history, the river is naturally changing course. Some areas where water has flowed for centuries are drying up while once-dry banks are now covered in water so that completely new paths are being created. Should it succeed in outwitting man, the Mississippi and its new path could devastate the cities of New Orleans and Baton Rouge. It is an extremely slow-motion confrontation, and the winner will not be declared for decades or even centuries to come.

As the River Turns

Read the time line of attempts at taming the Mississippi River below and then answer the questions that follow.

1718—The French develop New Orleans. An engineer working on city development demands that a dike be built to protect the town from Mississippi River flooding.

1718–1800—The growth of the cotton industry encourages the development of cities that rely on the waters of the Mississippi to transport their goods.

1718–1830—Individual property owners build and maintain levees that protected their properties only.

1831—A riverboat captain orders the construction of a channel to shortcut river navigation at Turnbull's Bend. This action and the 1839 blasting of a log jam in the region serve to encourage the Mississippi to reroute itself. Rerouting could place New Orleans and Baton Rouge beside swamp instead of fresh water.

1830s—Levee districts are developed to coordinate the efforts of individuals and to mandate levee maintenance.

1830–1840—The United States Army Corps contributes to levee construction and river widening when it improves river transportation. The federal government does not yet feel a constitutional right to work for flood protection, but only for commerce.

1849–1850—Intense flooding prompts the federal government to study potential flood control methods to be used in the lower Mississippi regions.

1861—The federal study concludes that levees will protect the region from floods.

1865–1880—The lower Mississippi Valley is divided into levee districts, and levees are constructed along the 700-mile stretch of the lower Mississippi.

1881–1890—Major floods affect the lower Mississippi region during six of these years. Volunteer guards patrol the levees night and day. When they detect leaks, entire villages work to maintain the embankment in time to prevent flooding. Guards also look out for strangers who might be "invaders" from the other side of the river attempting to relieve pressure on their own levees by sabotaging the other side.

1900—Dump wagons and mules replace wheelbarrows and men in building and maintaining levees.

1903—A major flood affects the Mississippi again, killing 40 people and costing $40 million.

1912, 1913—Major floods hit the lower Mississippi again.

1917—The federal government enters into an arrangement in which it splits the cost of levee building and maintenance with local governments 50–50.

1926—Heavy rains fall over the entire Mississippi drainage basin.

1927—The big flood hits.

1928—The Flood Control Act sets a precedent for federal oversight and financial support of flood control development. Numerous methods of control are employed on the Mississippi. Research and prediction centers are established and maintained.

1937—Another major flood affects the lower Mississippi killing 140 and causing $420 million worth of damage.

1954—The Army Corps of Engineers finally addresses the rerouting problem initiated in 1839 by building new dams, levees, and channels in an attempt to point the Mississippi in the desired direction.

1963—The Control Project is established to direct more monies and engineering genius to the rerouting problem.

1965—A Mississippi flood kills 20 and creates $180 million in damages.

1973—A major flood affects the Mississippi River again. Controls built by the 1963 Control Project are severely damaged.

1980s—The Army Corps begins to build another series of spillways in an attempt to ensure that the Mississippi River does not reroute where it would flow naturally.

1983—The lower Mississippi floods again.

1993—Severe flooding affects the upper and middle Mississippi Valley. Spring precipitation and snowmelt cannot be contained in the region's already saturated soils. Then a series of storms hits the region from June through August. Minnesota, Iowa, Illinois, and Missouri feel the effects of the flood the greatest. Over 1,000 levees fail, transportation suffers, 70,000 people are displaced, 50,000 homes are damaged, and 12,000 square miles of farmland are destroyed.

1. How many floods are reported in the time line? _____

2. River rerouting is a natural occurrence, but according to this time line, what human action prompted the Mississippi to reroute in a way it might not otherwise have done?

   _____

3. Why might levee districts have replaced the old system of individual property owners building and maintaining their own levees? _____

   _____

4. Why did the federal government only contribute to levee building that improved transportation during the 1830s and 1840s? _____

   _____

5. Has any flooding occurred along the Mississippi since the establishment of the Flood Control Act? _____

6. What caused the 1993 flooding of the upper and middle Mississippi? What states were most affected by the disaster?_____

   _____

   _____

Rescue Missions on the Mississippi

During the months-long 1927 Mississippi flood that affected residents of seven states, the Red Cross established 154 camps and assisted 325,000 flood victims. Unless you can put yourself in the shoes of one of those victims, 325,000 is just a number. Learn to appreciate what victims suffered on a more personal level by imagining yourself in one of the true rescue situations below. Write a letter describing your ordeal from one of the imaginary perspectives offered.

RESCUE ONE: About 500 people sought refuge on a mile-long bridge across the Arkansas River, when it overflowed as the Mississippi backed up into it. Winds and rushing waters made boat rescue missions impossible for three cold and rainy days and nights. During the long wait on the bridge, two women gave birth to babies. At last, all survivors were rescued by boat.

PERSPECTIVE ONE: You are one of the ladies who gave birth to a baby on the bridge. You floated atop a piece of lumber from the roof of your home for about four hours before reaching the bridge. Your husband, who carried you to your home's roof as the floodwaters rose, did not make it to the bridge. Although cold and wet for three days, desperately missing your husband, and aware that your home has been destroyed, you never lose hope that rescuers will arrive, and you and your baby will be okay. You are now in a warm hospital room ready to write a letter to your mother and father in New York. Describe your three-day ordeal, explaining the death of your husband, the destruction of your home, and birth of your child. Then ask your parents to send enough money for you and your baby to travel to New York so you can stay with them for a few months.

RESCUE TWO: William Faulkner described a four-day-long voyage of a small boat holding a convict and a woman he rescued during the flood. The tumbling waves rocked and rolled the boat and even landed it in a tree at one point. Still, it was picked up again before being deposited safely on an Indian mound.

PERSPECTIVE TWO: You are the convict. You were in prison for robbing three stores. You were released onto a boat when the jailhouse began to flood. Your release made you feel like you had been given a second chance at life. You decided to do only honest work from here on out. You began by rescuing a woman who bobbed in and out of the water about 200 yards away from you. The bumpy four-day ride atop rushing waves has been over now for three months. You now have a nice apartment and an honest job repairing appliances. You decide to write a letter to the woman you rescued thanking her for reminding you of the hero inside yourself.

RESCUE THREE: The small towns of St. Bernard and Plaquemines "rescued" New Orleans by sacrificing themselves. As the floodwaters approached densely populated New Orleans, it was determined that dynamiting a levee that protected the little towns would divert the threatening waters. Diver Ted Herbert planted 1,500 pounds of dynamite in the base of the Caernarvon Levee on his third attempt, and the towns of St. Bernard and Plaquemines were covered in water—their residents having transferred their goods and themselves to New Orleans—the city they saved.

PERSPECTIVE THREE: You are a former resident of St. Bernard. You packed two suitcases and a wheelbarrow of things from your home before making your way to New Orleans before your town's levee was dynamited. You have nothing else to your name. Still you want to see St. Bernard develop into a beautiful town again. Write to St. Bernard's mayor suggesting he unite the former citizens of his town in a mission to rebuild the community one home and business at a time.

RESCUE FOUR: Thousands of refugees lived in Red Cross tents that were raised on the portions of levees that remained intact near their homes. From their muddy new residences, they could see the roofs of their old homes bobbing in the river, but could retrieve nothing of their old lives.

PERSPECTIVE FOUR: You are an eight-year-old boy. Your parents, your four older sisters, and you have been living in a dirty tent for two weeks. Two-by-four planks have been placed in the mud to create a sidewalk from the hundreds of tents in your new "neighborhood" to the makeshift soup kitchen and outhouses. Your parents are sad and your sisters cry at night because your home has been destroyed along with your father's newspaper agency. You know you have no house to return to, but you cannot help but be a little bit happy. There are many boys to play with in the camp. You never have to take a bath. You don't even have new clothes to change into. The soup kitchen seldom has vegetables. From the edge of the levee you can watch houses bob and sink in the water, and you can catch worms and insects right outside your tent's door. Write a letter to a friend in a neighboring city admitting that you are enjoying your adventure.

RESCUE FIVE: Bootleggers who usually used their high-speed boats to transport illegal whiskey in the middle of the night, now used their boats to rescue their neighbors from rooftops and Indian mounds.

PERSPECTIVE FIVE: You are a police officer who was rescued by a bootlegger off the roof of your home. The man had been rescuing stranded flood victims for three days and nights by the time he got to you. You had arrested the bootlegger on two previous occasions when he had been caught transporting alcohol. The man was tired, hungry, and wet. He knew you could get him in trouble with the law again when the floodwaters receded. Still he rescued you. Write a letter informing the bootlegger that you would like to honor him at a formal ceremony for coming to your rescue and to the rescue of hundreds of others.

Taming the Tempest

Match the flood-controlling techniques employed following the Flood Control Act of 1928 with their descriptions below.

_____ 1. These huge complexes of concrete plates that have been chained together were laid on the Mississippi riverbank and riverbed at various places to prevent erosion.

_____ 2. While shortcuts to the Gulf of Mexico that the Mississippi creates naturally are not always located in desirable places, these man-made shortcuts encourage the river to flow where man would like it to flow.

_____ 3. These large chambers are built not only to give floodwaters a place to go, but also to act as storage banks for a city's water supply.

_____ 4. These raised embankments are effective on the Mississippi now that they are used in conjunction with other flood control methods.

_____ 5. This continuously employed procedure deepens the Mississippi so it can hold more water.

_____ 6. This replanting of trees along the banks of the Mississippi increases the soil's ability to absorb moisture.

_____ 7. These barriers are built on the tributaries to the Mississippi to prevent some waters from reaching the river.

_____ 8. These structures built atop, through, or around dams transport excess water downstream to prevent the flooding of a reservoir.

_____ 9. Recently, flood-prone major cities along the Mississippi have put in place these systems that can drain off billions of liters of water per day.

A. Dams

B. Cutoffs

C. Concrete Revetments

D. Levees

E. Dredging

F. Spillways

G. Reservoirs

H. Reforestation

I. Drainage Systems

Big Thompson Canyon:
Flood in a Flash

During the long weekend of Colorado's centennial, 3,000 outdoor enthusiasts filled the campsites and hotel rooms of Big Thompson Canyon. Scattered showers were forecasted for the afternoon of Saturday, July 31, 1976, but only a soft sprinkle fell by 5:30 p.m. The canyon was receiving the precipitation of a line of thunderstorms that stretched from central Kansas to eastern Colorado. Vacationers were not dissuaded from hiking trails or fishing streams by the light rain. Even local residents were unconcerned. They knew that most thunderstorms over the Colorado Rockies drift quickly—and uneventfully—to the east. The July 31 storm, however, did not drift.

The Big Thompson thunderstorm stubbornly stalled directly over the canyon. Visitors who felt the sprinkles at 5:30 p.m. described the descent of "half-inch raindrops" by eight o'clock. The stationary storm dropped 10 inches of rain in the 25-mile region from Loveland to Estes Park, Colorado. Overflowing streams and rivulets rushed into the steep and narrow canyon. Big Thompson was overwhelmed quickly. Its rocky sides absorbed almost no water, and its narrow passages became blocked with debris. Near the city of Drake, halfway down the canyon, the river raced at over 31,000 cubic feet of water per second as opposed to the 137 cubic feet it was accustomed to carrying.

The canyon's rushing waters began to smash cars, camping trailers, and tents into sharp-edged boulders. Uprooted trees, houses, and stores swept down the river. Speeding debris acted as battering rams smashing into structures downstream and blocking narrow passages so that even more water backed up into the canyon. Thousands of terrified campers scrambled up the jagged walls of the canyon where they shivered in the night atop cold, hard rocks awaiting morning rescue rides in helicopters. Over a hundred others died in their cars when Highway 34 was washed away.

For hours, no one on the outside knew of the horrors within the canyon. The string of Kansas and Colorado storms that bore the Big Thompson disaster had dissipated in all other regions. Weather radar underestimated the size of the area still receiving heavy rains. A Denver forecaster predicted at 7:35 p.m. that some low area flooding was possible. By 9:00 p.m., he warned that the slow movement of the storm could result in "some local flooding." Even the nearby Estes Park police, responding to an 8:00 p.m. report that a portion of Highway 34 had washed away, did not know the extent of the flood until they drove into the canyon region. Not until 11:00 p.m. did Denver forecasters get word directly from the scene.

In the end, 139 people had been killed by the flood and hundreds of others injured. The flood also destroyed 418 homes along with 52 businesses. Over $35 million worth of damage had been caused by the thunderstorm that would not move. Following the disaster, residents and businesses were prohibited from rebuilding too near the river, and signs were erected warning, "Climb to safety in case of a flash flood."

Flash Flood Facts

Match the first and last parts of sentences below to make true statements about flash floods. The first one has been done for you.

Sentence Starters

1. Drivers should not attempt to drive through floodwaters, not only because their vehicles might stall or be swept away by the waters, but also because __C__.
2. If you drive into a flooded area and find yourself blocked by floodwaters or a washed-out road, _____.
3. Most victims of natural disasters are not victims because they panic, but rather because _____.
4. Because flash floods cannot be predicted by long-range forecasting, some flood plain regions have installed warning systems that ring bells when _____.
5. While floods on larger rivers can often be forecasted days in advance, smaller streams _____.
6. Normally the Big Thompson River is more of a _____.
7. Sometimes victims of a flash flood have no idea they are in danger because _____.
8. While flash floods in the East are often the result of a heavy rain falling on hard, dry soil that cannot absorb much water, flash floods in the West _____.
9. America's most deadly flash flood was caused by _____.
10. While regular floods can affect hundreds of square miles and last for weeks, _____.
11. In Southeast Asia, flash floods kill _____.
12. Flash floods occur on almost a routine basis in some highly populated areas of the world including _____.

Sentence Enders

A. . . . they refuse to heed the warnings of the National Weather Service.
B. . . . trickling stream than a river.
C. . . . the road under the water might be washed away.
D. . . . rainfall and/or stream levels in the region rise to dangerous levels.
E. . . . are usually the result of snowmelt and heavy rains, adding to already saturated soils.
F. . . . get out of your car and climb to higher ground.
G. . . . usually experience flash floods that come without prior warning.
H. . . . floodwaters can rush miles downstream and affect regions that are experiencing bright, sunny weather.
 I. . . . hundreds of people annually and destroy millions of acres of crops.
J. . . . flash floods can sometimes have a lifespan of only a few minutes.
K. . . . the collapse of a poorly built dam in Johnstown, Pennsylvania.
L. . . . the region around Rio de Janeiro, Brazil.

Flashes, Crashes, and Hailstones

Thunderstorms not only cause flash floods like the one at Big Thompson Canyon, but they also produce lightning, thunder, and hailstones. Determine which term from the box fits each description below. Each term will be used several times. The first one has been completed for you.

Thunderstorms   Thunder   Lightning   Hailstones   Thunderclouds

__Thunderstorms__ 1. Nearly 2,000 of these are in progress around the globe at any time.

_____ 2. This strikes earth about 100 times per second.

_____ 3. The reason these build up electrical charges is not yet well understood. Both a convection and a precipitation theory try to explain the process.

_____ 4. These water droplets freeze and gather ice and dust as they bounce around in a thunder cloud, moving upward due to convection and back down due to gravity.

_____ 5. This phenomenon can cause fires, damage airplanes, split trees in half, and kill animals and people.

_____ 6. Two thirds of people close enough to receive a shock when this strikes do not die.

_____ 7. These seldom grow to a size larger than a pea.

_____ 8. These occur because of temperature imbalances in the atmosphere.

_____ 9. These cumulonimbus clouds can be several miles across and over 40,000 feet tall.

_____ 10. This noise occurs because lightning heats the air to over 50,000 degrees Fahrenheit—about four times the temperature of the surface of the sun. The heat expands the air, and the cooling that follows contracts it to create a "boom."

_____ 11. This travels down from a cloud and then sends a return strike back up at one third of the speed of light.

_____ 12. This sound reaches you a few seconds after you see lightning strike.

_____ 13. These can become the size of eggs, baseballs, or grapefruits if held in a cloud long enough by updrafts approaching 100 miles per hour.

_____ 14. These contain a sandwich-like stacking of positive and negative charges that are released when lightning strikes.

_____ 15. These cause billions of dollars in crop damages and millions in livestock deaths and property damage each year.

_____ 16. This can be caused by rocket exhausts, tornadoes, volcanoes, or nuclear explosions as well as by thunderstorms.

_____ 17. If you hear this sound five seconds after you see lightning, the lightning you saw was one mile away.

_____ 18. Evaluating the time, duration, pitch, and loudness of this helps researchers determine the length, direction, altitude, and energy of lightning.

_____ 19. These are usually composed of several thundercells.

_____ 20. This can travel within a cloud, from cloud to cloud, or from cloud to ground in the shape of a streak or even a ball.

Answer Key

Volcanic Vocabulary   **page 3**

Volcanic Activity

2. *Dormant volcanoes* are thought to be "sleeping." Although they are not presently active, they could conceivably become active in the foreseeable future.
3. Although *extinct volcanoes* were active in the past, they are not expected to become active again in the foreseeable future.

Volcanic Materials

1. *Tephra* is a general term that refers to any material released from a volcano.
2. *Pahoehoe* is a type of lava that looks like thick coils of rope.
3. *Aa* is a lava with a rough and jagged surface.
4. *Lapilli* means "little stones" and refers to solid or molten rock fragments ejected from an erupting volcano.
5. *Limuopele* is sheets of lava filled with glass bubbles.
6. *Pele's tears* are solidified drops of tear-shaped volcanic glass.
7. *Nuée ardente* refers to gas-charged ash that speeds down a mountainside with explosive force.
8. *Bombs* are plastic-like, semi-molten rocks that take any number of forms as they are ejected from an erupting volcano.
9. *Blocks* are angular, solid rocks that are thrown from a volcano.
10. *Ash* refers to the fine particles that can be either solid or molten when erupted from a volcano.

Eruption Styles

1. A *strombolian* eruption takes place when a volcano releases fountains of fluid lava from a central crater.
2. The highly explosive *volcanian* eruption ejects blocks of hard lava.
3. A *Plinian* eruption is characterized by massive amounts of tephra, tall columns of smoke and ash, and a highly explosive release of magma and gases at a high velocity.
4. *Hawaiian* eruptions take place from the side of volcanoes rather than from the central crater.

Volcanic Rock

1. *Basalt* is a dark rock comprised of about 50% silica and a fair amount of iron and magnesium.
2. *Dacite* is a light-colored lava that contains a large amount of silica.
3. *Rhyolite* is light-colored lava rich in potassium and sodium and containing abut 69% silica.
4. *Andesite* is medium-colored lava containing about 55% silica and some iron and magnesium.
5. *Ignimbrite* is the rock formed when ash flows and nuée ardente consolidate.
6. *Obsidian* is dark volcanic glass.
7. *Pumice* is a porous volcanic glass formed by the expansion of gas in lava.

Classifying Volcanoes   **page 4**

1. Submarine volcanoes
2. Monogenetic field
3. Composite volcanoes
4. Submarine volcanoes
5. Composite volcanoes
6. Caldera volcanoes
7. Shield volcanoes
8. Caldera volcanoes
9. Caldera volcanoes
10. Composite volcanoes

So You Want to Be a Volcanologist?   **page 5**

1. T
2. F, The most important science a volcanologist can study is geology, the study of the earth's rocks.
3. T
4. F, Most volcanologists' assistants and technicians hold bachelors' degrees.
5. F, Although many volcanologists work for the U.S. Geological Survey, *most* teach college courses in geology and study volcanoes in the summers.
6. T
7. T

8. F, Most colleges do not offer courses in volcanology. Volcanologists who teach in universities most often teach traditional geology courses.
9. F, Few colleges offer volcanology courses. Volcanologists major in geology.
10. T
11. F, Physical volcanologists study volcanic eruptions.
12. F, Geochemists study the composition of volcanic products.
13. F, Few jobs are available for volcanologists today.
14. T
15. T

Valuable Volcanoes   **page 6**

1. Soil and mineral benefits
2. Energy benefits
3. Energy benefits
4. Commercial benefits
5. Soil and mineral benefits
6. Energy benefits
7. Commercial benefits
8. Soil and mineral benefits
9. Soil and mineral benefits
10. Commercial benefits

Safety During Volcanic Eruptions   **page 8**

2. During
3. During
4. Before
5. Before
6. After
7. Before
8. During
9. During, After
10. During, After
11. During
12. Before
13. During

Herculaneum, City of Hercules   **page 9**

1. The myth of Hercules might attempt to explain the existence of human strength and courage. It also explains the concept of penance, or consequences. The havoc that Hera plays in Hercules' life acknowledges the existence of "bad luck" or the encountering of fate—circumstances that seem beyond human control.
2. Student opinion
3. Myths and tall tales both exaggerate accomplishments. They are both at least partially fictional accounts of incredible characters. Tall tales do not usually involve gods or goddesses. Tall tales only sometimes attempt to explain reality.

Archeological Information   **page 10**

2. Hypothesis: The resident of the home is a college student. Proof: College-level textbooks and paper and pencil on the desk
   Hypothesis: The resident of the home plays college football. Proof: Sweat pants, football helmet, and football jersey
3. Hypothesis: One of the residents of this home is a baby. Proof: Disney wallpaper, diapers, baby food
   Hypothesis: One of the residents of this home likes to cook. Proof: Baking goods on counter, spices, full pantry, and refrigerator
4. Hypothesis: A resident of this home works on cars. Proof: Garage with jacked-up car, oil stains, auto parts, and jumper
   Hypothesis: The person who works on cars is a woman. Proof: Size of jumper, presence of barrettes, and diamond ring

One Survivor's Story   **page 14**

1. The residents of neighboring islands were surprised by the great explosion of Krakatau both because tremors were common and expected on the islands and because Krakatau was believed to be extinct.
2. The Beyerincks survived the explosion by getting away from the beach that was hit by the tsunami and locking themselves inside a home on the middle of the island until the burning explosive materials had fallen.
3. Natural disasters hit all people in their paths regardless of age, race, sex, or religion, injuring and killing people at random. Since they destroy property, they also turn rich people into poor and render kings as temporarily homeless as paupers.

4. The personal account of a disaster helps a reader to relate to the experience in a more emotional way than can reports of facts and statistics.

Avalanche · page 15
1. 5
2. 100; 30; 20; 4
3. 96
4. 1/5
5. 1
6. 50
7. 324
8. 100,000
9. 10; 4,000
10. 18,000
11. 110
12. 45

Understanding Lakes · page 17
2. rainfall, springs, rivers
3. one half
4. evaporation, lack of precipitation, swamps
5. industrial pollution
6. glacier-margin lake
7. Glacial-deposition
8. Lake Superior, Caspian Sea
9. Lake Baikal, 5,371 feet, one fifth
10. salt, sulfates, carbonates

Craters and Calderas · page 19
1. Alaska, U.S.
2. New Zealand
3. Japan
4. Oregon, U.S.
5. Greece
6. Réunion Island
7. Italy
8. Oregon, U.S.
9. Alaska, U.S.
10. Indonesia
11. Mexico
12. France
13. Hawaii, U.S.
14. France
15. Greece
16. Indonesia
17. Washington, U.S.

Mapping the Cascade Range · page 21
The volcanoes to be identified by students should be in the following ordering beginning in the north and going south (from top to bottom of map): Mount Baker, Glacier Peak, Mount Rainier, Mount Saint Helens (left), Mount Adams (right), Mount Hood, Mount Jefferson, Three Sisters, Newberry Volcano, Crater Lake, Mount McLoughlin, Medicine Lake (right), Mount Shasta (left)

Volcanic Studies · page 22
2. A
3. A
4. B
5. A
6. B
7. B
8. A
9. B
10. A
11. A
12. A

Twentieth-Century Eruptions · page 23
1. D
2. A
3. E
4. B
5. C
6. F
7. G

Pinpointing Potential Problems · page 26
The Circum-Pacific Belt wraps around the edges of the Pacific Ocean, and the Alpide Belt, also known as the Mediterranean zone, begins at the top of Africa and follows the line between Europe and Asia—south through the Indian Ocean—and north through the Atlantic Ocean, where it runs along midocean ridges all the way past Greenland.

Studying the Earth's Vibrations · page 27
1. C
2. G
3. B
4. D
5. H
6. A
7. E
8. F

Aftershocks and Body Waves · page 28

Fighting Fires · page 30
A HISTORY OF FIRE FIGHTING should include facts about Emperor Augustus' watchmen, the fire brigade established by insurance companies (and eventually overtaken by the government) in London following the Great Fire of London in 1666, and Ben Franklin's fire company. This section could also include a history of fire engines.
MODERN FIRE DEPARTMENTS should include information about the career firefighters employed by large cities and the volunteer departments of smaller towns.
FIRE PREVENTION should include information on alarm systems, sprinkler systems, smoke detectors, building codes, and inflammable materials.
FIGHTING FIRES should include information on fire engines, fire boats, and auxiliary equipment, such as protective clothing, ladders, axes, and battering rams. This section could also discuss types of fires and the water and/or chemicals used to combat each.

Earthquakes in Review · page 31
2. True
3. False—Major earthquakes seem to occur once every few hundred years along major faults.
4. True
5. True
6. False—The time and place of a major quake cannot be predicted, but zone maps are drawn and assigned danger levels, and the probability of an earthquake occurring in a region over a long period of time is forecasted.
7. True
8. False—The opposite is true.
9. False—The opposite is true.
10. True

Warning! Tsunami Approaching! · page 33
During
1. No, a tsunami warning is issued only when a tsunami threat exists. Evacuate immediately when such a warning is issued for your area.
2. No, if you can see a tsunami wave, you are too close for safety!

3. No, tsunamis can comprise a series of waves. The second or third may be stronger than the first. Do not return to your home until instructed to do so by authorities.

After
1. Yes
2. Yes
3. No, Remove mud immediately so that walls and floors can dry out.
4. Yes
5. Yes
6. No, Open doors and windows to dry out a flood-damaged home.

Turning Disaster into Delight   page 36
Although answers will vary, possible responses follow:
1. You could apologize to the boy in front of your friends, stick up for him in the future, make a concerted effort to get to know him as a person, and/or make it your mission to stamp out name-calling and ridicule at your school.
2. You could apologize to the man offended by your group's noise and not only keep quiet yourself but remind your friends to do the same.
3. Learning from your mistake, you could vow to finish homework and study for tests before enjoying after-school activities in the future. You could also seek help from a friend, complete extra credit assignments, or discuss with your teacher how to make up for your poor exam score.
4. You could apologize to your mother or even make her a card, write her a letter, or cook her favorite dinner.
5. You could not only pay to replace the window but make all the phone calls and arrangements necessary for getting it replaced. You could also remember to keep outside activities outside in the future.
6. You could practice speaking and performing in front of friends and relatives until you feel more comfortable in front of large groups. You could concentrate on the importance of public-speaking skills and ask your teacher for suggestions for dealing with stage fright.
7. You could attend art classes offered in your community in the evenings or summers. You could start an art club at school. You could check out books on art from the library and teach yourself skills at home. You could locate a talented artist in your community who could instruct you. You could use art in your other classes when given project options. You could offer to make signs for school projects and backdrops for school plays so that you could use your talents even if an actual class is not offered.

Measuring Quakes and Shakes   page 37
1. The Richter Scale
2. Mercalli's Scale
3. Rating 2-3
4. Mercalli's Scale
5. Mercalli's Scale
6. The Richter Scale
7. Mercalli's Scale attempts to be more lay-person friendly.
8. Student Opinion; Support for using either scale could be given.

Rescue Missions   page 38
Rescuing Techniques: Statements 1, 4, 6, 7, 10
Rescuing Difficulties: Statements 2, 3, 5, 8, 9

Mapping Disaster   page 40
1. B
2. Missouri
3. Lake Itasca, Minnesota, to the Gulf of Mexico
4. Pittsburgh, Pennsylvania
5. Memphis is located at letter A and Cairo at letter C.
6. D
7. Arkansas
8. Missouri

John James Audubon   page 41
1. The work of John Audubon continued to be appreciated after his death in 1851.
2. During his lifetime, John James Audubon lived in Haiti, France, England, and the United States.
3. John Audubon studied and drew pictures of American birds.
4. The Scottish naturalist William MacGillivray was instrumental in transforming *The Birds of America* into more than just a picture book.

Great Earthquakes Worldwide   page 42
1. C
2. E
3. A
4. F
5. G
6. B
7. H
8. D

I Didn't Know That!   page 47
1. T
2. F—Although this was once thought to be true, it is now known that the tornado's *winds,* which can blow a roof off a house and cause its walls to crash outward, are responsible for the appearance of explosion, and *not* the tornado's low pressure center.
3. T
4. T
5. F—Tornadoes are not quiet! The noise resulting from their concentrated winds touching ground sounds like a jet plane taking off or a locomotive approaching.
6. T
7. F—Most tornadoes occur in either April, May, or June.
8. T
9. F—A hurricane intensifies as the eye of the storm *shrinks.*
10. T
11. T
12. F—Hurricane formation requires the ocean waters to be over 80 degrees Fahrenheit.
13. T
14. F—Thunderstorms organized into a swirl over an ocean are called *tropical depressions.* They are not labeled tropical storms until their winds exceed 39 m.p.h.
15. T
16. T
17. T
18. T
19. F—A tornado is seldom a mile across, while the diameter of a hurricane can range from 300–400 miles.
20. T

Thunderstorms Gone Mad   page 48
The Fujita Wind Damage Scale:
F0 A
F1 C
F2 F
F3 D
F4 B
F5 E

The Saffir-Simpson Damage-Potential Scale:
1 D
2 A
3 E
4 C
5 B

Barrier Islands From Texas to Maine   **page 50**
1. Louisiana   Circle:
2. Georgia   New Orleans
3. Texas   Jacksonville
4. Mississippi   St. Petersburg
5. Alabama   Norfolk
6. South Carolina   Corpus Christi
7. Louisiana
8. Rhode Island   Underline:
9. Maine   Birmingham
10. Massachusetts   Atlanta
11. New York   Columbia
12. Maine
13. Florida
14. South Carolina
15. South Carolina
16. Massachusetts
17. New York
18. Maine
19. Florida
20. New York

Elevated Warnings   **page 54**
1. A   3. C
2. D   4. B

What's in a Name?   **page 55**
Before 1950   1952-1978
1860—Hurricane I   Hurricane Audrey
The Great Hurricane of 1780   Hurricane Eloise
The Late Gale at St. Joseph   Hurricane Hazel

1950-1952   1978-Present
Hurricane King   Hurricane Hugo
Hurricane Easy   Hurricane George
Hurricane Able   Hurricane Mitch

Twentieth-Century Hurricanes   **page 56**
2. 1935 Florida Keys Hurricane
3. Hurricane Agnes
4. Hurricane Hazel
5. Hurricane Hugo
6. Hurricane Elena
7. Hurricane Fredric
8. Hurricane Andrew
9. New England Hurricane of 1938

The Great Hurricane of 1780   **page 58**
2. A   7. I
3. E   8. K
4. B   9. F
5. H   10. J
6. C   11. G

Hurricane Heroes   **page 59**
1. B   4. E
2. C   5. F
3. D   6. A

Watches and Warnings   **page 62**
1. True
2. False—Seek shelter in an inner hallway or inner small room
   with no windows, such as a closet.
3. True
4. False—Get out of the mobile home and seek shelter elsewhere.
   Many mobile home parks provide an underground community
   shelter.
5. True
6. True
7. False—Never try to outrun a tornado. Seek a basement or
   small inner room inside the building where you find yourself at
   the time of the warning.
8. False—Buildings with large roof spans are especially dangerous
   in a tornado.

Before and After
1. before   7. after
2. after   8. after
3. after   9. before
4. before   10. after
5. before   11. after
6. before

Famous Funnels   **page 63**
1. Great Southern Tornado Outbreak of 1884
2. May 1948 Tornado of McKinney, Texas
3. Great Natchez Tornado of May 1840
4. Worcester County, Massachusetts, Tornado of 1953
5. Viroqua, Wisconsin, Tornado: June 28, 1865
6. Kansas Turnpike Tornado
7. Hurricane Beulah

A Blizzard A'Blowin'   **page 65**
Home Preparations: 1, 4, 7, 12
Staying Informed: 2, 6, 9, 15, 19
Travel Preparations: 3, 8, 13, 17
If You Get Stranded in a Car: 5, 10, 11, 14, 16, 18

Reading the Sky   **page 67**
1. Stratus   6. Cumulonimbus
2. Cirrus   7. Nimbostratus
3. Cirrocumulus   8. Altocumulus
4. Stratocumulus   9. Altostratus
5. Cumulus

Worthwhile Wind   **page 69**
2. By turning a fan inside the appliance, a vacuum cleaner forces
   air quickly to fill in a vacuum, suctioning in dirt along with the
   air to clean a room.
3. Water pumps use suction to force water up a long pipe.
4. A boat sail uses moving air to help push a boat along the
   surface of a lake.
5. Air drills use pressurized air to break up surfaces in
   preparation to lay or repair roads.
6. Air brakes use pressurized air to stop trucks.
7. Sand blasters use pressurized air to clean large surfaces.
8. Spray bottles use pressurized air to spray water or other
   liquids.
9. Parachutes use the air to slow down the landing of a person
   who jumps from a plane.
10. Pressurized air keeps a basketball firm.
11. Spores and seeds travel on the wind.
12. Air vibrates across the mouthpiece or in a large horn of brass
    and wind instruments.
13. Airplane wings use airflow to give them lift.
14. The colors of a sunset result from light being reflected off
    particles suspended in the air.
15. Hot air balloons use the lightness of heated air to keep them
    afloat.

Knowing the Numbers   **page 70**
1. A. 5,490   B. 475   C. 7,452   D. 19
2. A. 886   B. 16
3. A. 0
4. A. 82   B. 1
5. A. 83

Defining Droughts   **page 73**
1. Definitions 5 and 6   5. Definition 2
2. Definition 1   6. Definition 1
3. Definition 4   7. Definitions 2, 4, and 6
4. Definition 3   8. Definition 5

Horrifyingly Hot   **page 74**
1. ...the body must overwork to keep its internal temperature
   constant.
2. ...overexposure to heat, overexercise, or exposure to poor air
   conditions caused by smog, smoke, or other pollutants.

3. ...temperatures that remain ten or more degrees above the average high temperature for a region for several weeks.
4. ...sunburn, heat stroke, heat exhaustion, and dehydration.
5. ...the young, old, sick, and overweight.
6. 175
7. ...they become more quickly dehydrated because they sweat more.
8. ...a sunburn slows the body's ability to cool itself.
9. ...pollutants in the city become trapped by the stagnant air of the heat wave.
10. ...they keep the heat out in the summer just as they do the cold in the winter.
11. 80
12. ...move the warm air around the room.
13. ...they dehydrate your body further.
14. ...loose, lightweight, light-colored clothing that covers as much skin as possible.
15. ...doing so could cause hypothermia.
16. ...to take a soap-and-water shower to clear pores of oil so the body can cool itself naturally.
17. ...heat spasms.
18. ...sweating, weakness, clammy skin, weak pulse, vomiting, and fainting.
19. ...body temperature as high as 106 degrees or more, hot skin, dry skin, rapid pulse, and possible unconsciousness.
20. ...get immediate medical assistance! Heat stroke can be fatal. Call 911. Do not give water. Remove clothing of victim and provide cool bath and air conditioning.

Hot and Dry Verbiage   **page 75**
1. The *hydrologic cycle* is the circulation of water from land to oceans to atmosphere and back again.
2. An *aquifer* is an underground layer of porous rock that holds water.
3. *Desertification* is the transformation of arable land to desert.
4. *Black blizzard* is another term for drought-related dust storms.
5. The verb *desiccate* means to dry out.
6. The clearing away of the trees of a forest for the sake of farming or development is called *deforestation*.
7. *Arid* land is dry land that lacks substantial rainfall.
8. A *dry spell* is a short-lived drought, usually defined as 14 days without precipitation.
9. *Arable land* is land fit for cultivation.
10. *Overcropping* occurs when land is cultivated so frequently that it is not given the opportunity to reestablish its proper nutrient level before the next crop is planted.
11. *Ground water* is the water under the ground that supplies springs and wells.
12. *Runoff* refers to precipitation which flows into streams and rivers, which flow into the oceans.
13. The Great Plains region that was affected by a ten-year drought during the thirties was sometimes referred to as the *dust bowl* or the *Dirty Thirties*.
14. A *famine* is a widespread food shortage.
15. A *maelstrom* is a whirlpool. Dust storms sometimes take the form of maelstroms.

Waste Not, Want Not   **page 76**
2. 10 gallons. Do not leave water running while you brush; turn on only to wet brush and to rinse.
3. 45 gallons. Wash dishes in sink full of water to decrease water usage to 5 gallons.
4. 14 gallons. Use the short cycle and only wash *full* loads of dishes.
5. 35 gallons. Use the short cycle, use the lowest level of water reasonable for the size of your load, and wear around-the-house clothes more than once before each wash.
6. 60 gallons. Do not fill the tub.
7. 25 gallons. Install low-capacity showerhead, take shorter showers, and/or turn off water while lathering.
8. 20 gallons. Fill the sink with water instead of letting it run while you shave.

9. 2 gallons. Wash hands in a sink *full* of water instead of under a running tap.

Respecting the Water Cycle   **page 78**
1. Purpose—Bring water to dry lands
   Consequence—Water reserves from wet areas can be depleted to irrigate dry areas.
2. Purpose—Wells provide drinking and irrigation water.
   Consequence—Excessive pumping depletes aquifers and introduces salt into fresh water.
3. Purpose—Redirect rivers for the purpose of storage, navigation, or electricity manufacturing
   Consequence—Run-off water is not permitted to run its natural course.
4. Purpose—Create urban centers
   Consequence—Paved areas allow runoff water to reach streams more quickly causing flooding in some regions.
5. Purpose—Trees are used as building material and as fuel and are cut down to make room for the cultivation of crops.
   Consequence—Deforestation depletes soils of their nutrients and reduces their ability to absorb moisture.
6. Purpose—Make rain fall on drought-affected areas
   Consequence—Causing a cloud to rain in one area prevents it from raining in another.

Roosevelt to the Rescue   **page 79**
1. The Agricultural Adjustment Act of 1933 paid farmers to reduce their crops and livestock production. Although it was aimed at boosting farm prices all over the country by reducing the supply of meat and grains, it specifically assisted dust bowlers who could not cultivate much of their land anyway, due to drought conditions.
2. The Emergency Farm Mortgage Act of 1933 allowed farmers whose crops and/or farm equipment had been destroyed by the drought and dust storms to borrow money to purchase new equipment and seed.
3. The Resettlement Administration Act of 1935 moved farmers from unfertile farms to new lands.
4. The Soil Conservation Act of 1936 paid farmers to use new agricultural methods designed to conserve topsoil and reduce the risk of dust storms. The act was effective in reducing soil loss by 65% in 1937.
5. The Farm Security Administration of 1937 loaned money to tenant farmers to help them buy their own farms. In the dust bowl region this promoted the farming of lands abandoned by those defeated by the drought.

Conserving the Soil   **page 81**
Hugh Bennett was a leading agricultural expert in the 1920s and 1930s who condemned Americans as "the greatest destroyers of land of any race or people barbaric or civilized." He took on the challenge of changing that fact himself. He vigorously campaigned Congress to pass the Soil Conservation Act and introduced farmers to soil conservation techniques, such as contour farming, controlled grazing, crop alternating, and windbreak constructing. At one meeting with Congress he took a unique approach to making his point that a loss of topsoil meant a loss of a land's ability to retain water. Without speaking a single word, he and his colleague, Walter Lowdermilk, poured a glass of water on top of a bath towel which they had placed atop a table on the Senate floor. Then they removed the towel and poured another glass of water directly onto the table top so that the liquid dripped into the laps of our nation's senators.
1. C   4. E
2. B   5. A
3. F   6. D

Definitely Dry   **page 83**
2. True
3. True
4. True
5. False—Only 20% of the cover is sand; the rest is fertile soil when irrigated.

6. False—Rainfall in the region averages 4-8 inches annually.
7. True
8. True
9. True
10. False—The Nile, which flows across the Sahara, is the world's longest river.
11. True
12. True
13. True
14. True
15. False—The economy thrives on oil and mineral deposits.
16. True
17. True
18. True
19. True
20. False—Egypt is in the Sahara region.

More Definitely Dry   page 84
1. one third
2. one fifth
3. one half
4. the deserts of Peru
5. 12 percent
6. the United States
7. 20,000
8. 50
9. 10
10. low
11. Gobi
12. Australia
13. few days
14. Woody
15. small
16. after
17. during the day
18. full of
19. river
20. 35

Desert Dwellers   page 85
1. Marco Polo
2. Charles Sturt
3. Heinrich Barth
4. Ibn Battuta

Refraining from Fanning the Flames   page 88
2. Emergency procedures
3. Emergency procedures
4. Routine precautions
5. Routine precautions
6. Emergency procedures
7. Routine precautions
8. Emergency procedures
9. Emergency procedures
10. Routine precautions
11. Routine precautions
12. Emergency procedures
13. Routine precautions
14. Emergency procedures
15. Routine precautions
16. Routine precautions

Drip, Drop, Drought   page 92
2. year round
3. during droughts
4. year round
5. during droughts
6. during droughts
7. during droughts
8. year round
9. during droughts
10. year round
11. year round
12. during droughts
13. year round
14. year round
15. year round

Flood Facts   page 97
1. False—Drowning is the number one cause of deaths during floods. Electrocution comes in second.
2. False—80% of people who drown in floods do so in automobiles.
3. True
4. True
5. True
6. False—Modern research indicates that levees alone are not sufficient to prevent floods. In the case of the Yellow River levees, the raised embankments caused sediment to settle in the river only instead of all over the floodplain. So, the river bed rose so dramatically during 4,000 years time, that by 1887, a flood broke through the levees and killed more than one million people.
7. True
8. True
9. False—Flood waters can move at such a fast and powerful pace that they can uproot trees, sweep away bridges, and float automobiles.
10. True
11. True
12. False—The United States has only 13 river forecasting centers.
13. True
14. True
15. True
16. True
17. False—If you cannot see the bottom of the water, do not attempt to wade through it.
18. True
19. False—the acre foot is a measurement of how much water it would take to cover one acre in one foot of water.
20. True
21. False—Six percent of the land in the United States is prone to flooding.
22. False—Cities were settled near rivers because rivers provided the only means of transportation before the invention of railways, automobiles, and airplanes.
23. False—Over 20,000 American communities face occasional flooding problems.

Drying Out   page 98
1. Walls
2. Appliances
3. Windows
4. Clothing and Linens
5. Computer Disks
6. Furniture
7. Kitchen Items
8. The Lawn
9. Papers and Books
10. Food
11. The Yard

100% Chance of Rain   page 99
1. B, D
2. C
3. E, G
4. A
5. F, I
6. H

Look Out Below!   page 101
1. Mudslides can be triggered by heavy thunderstorms, flash floods, regular floods, earthquakes, or volcanoes. Deforestation and the development of landslide-prone regions increases their occurrence.
2. Yes
3. Mudslides are difficult to study because the behavior of mud is not exactly like that of a liquid or a solid and because mudslides occur so unpredictably and are over so quickly.
4. Landslide-prone regions are developed because people are drawn to their rich soils and their great views, and because mudslides occur so infrequently that new residents are not aware that their home is built on vulnerable ground.
5. Mudslide controls include debris dams, restraining structures, slope grading, drainage systems, zoning codes, building codes, and landslide-warning systems.
6. The 18,000 mudslides that occurred in the San Francisco region in 1982 attest to the fact that the American west coast is susceptible to mudslides. So do the 1982 mudslides in Colombia following Hurricane Mitch in 1998, and the fact that 20,000 people in Colombia were killed by landslides in 1985. Some of the deaths and damages caused by landslides also occurred on the west coast of the United States.

The Yangtze: The Yellow River's Southern Sister   page 102
1. Negative—Destroys property and kills wildlife and sometimes people. Positive—Thins out forests that are dying and/or too thick. Makes way for new growth.
2. Negative—Destroys property and kills wildlife and sometimes people. Positive—Ash creates fertile soil. Makes way for new growth.
3. Negative—Destroys property and kills wildlife and people. Positive—Provides rich soil and changes the direction of rivers and modifies other geographical formations as nature would have it.
4. Negative—Starts fires, topples buildings, injures and kills people. Positive—Nature's method of moving tectonic plates as it sees fit.
5. Negative—Destroys property and injures and kills people. Positive—The thunderstorms that create the tornadoes act as nature's cooling system.

6. Negative—Destroys property and injures and kills people. Positive—The storms that create hurricanes also serve to adjust the temperature of the atmosphere.

The Effects of El Niño
page 103
1. T
2. T
3. F—El Niños slow easterly winds across the tropical Pacific to an almost standstill.
4. F—The El Niño effect increases hurricane activity in the North Pacific, but it decreases it in the North Atlantic.
5. T
6. F—Alaska experienced warmer and drier weather than normal that season.
7. T—Incidentally, the region is accustomed to only one typhoon every three years.
8. T
9. F—Stronger than normal trade winds predict El Niños.
10. T
11. T
12. F—El Niños can affect the entire globe.
13. T
14. F—Fish and birds die or leave the region during El Niños.
15. T
16. F—The most severe El Niño of the twentieth century occurred in 1982–1983.

The Great Potato Famine
page 104
1. False—The potato is an underground tuber that does not develop from the plant's blossoms.
2. True
3. False—Refrigeration turns potato starches into sugars. Store them instead in a cool, dark place.
4. False—A potato provides 9% of your recommended dietary fiber for a day and 20% of your potassium.
5. True
6. True
7. False—A medium potato contains about 120 calories.
8. True
9. True
10. False—Thomas Jefferson introduced the french fry at a White House dinner.
11. False—Potato production worldwide is second only to wheat.
12. True
13. False—Potatoes originated in South America.
14. True
15. True

Natural Weather Forecasters
page 107
1. B
2. H
3. A
4. I
5. E
6. C
7. L
8. G
9. K
10. F
11. J
12. D

Worldwide Flooding
page 108
1. Bangladesh
2. South Dakota
3. Paraguay
4. Missouri
5. Mid-Atlantic States
6. Georgia
7. Northwestern Europe
8. California
9. Ohio
10. Colombia
11. India
12. Italy

As the River Turns
pages 110 and 111
1. 15
2. The 1831 construction of an artificial channel for the purpose of shortcutting transportation influenced river rerouting.
3. Since the integrity of levees all along the river affects the entire region, organization was required to ensure all levees were maintained.
4. The Constitution specifically gave the federal government authority in issues concerning commerce, but not in those concerning disasters.
5. Yes
6. Heavy spring rains and melting snow saturated the soil of the region so that it could not contain the waters of the heavy rains that fell from June through August. Minnesota, Iowa, Illinois, and Missouri were the most affected by the flood waters.

Taming the Tempest
page 114
1. C
2. B
3. G
4. D
5. E
6. H
7. A
8. F
9. I

Flash Flood Facts
page 116
1. C
2. F
3. A
4. D
5. G
6. B
7. H
8. E
9. K
10. J
11. I
12. L

Flashes, Crashes, and Hailstones
page 117
1. Thunderstorms
2. Lightning
3. Thunderclouds
4. Hailstones
5. Lightning
6. Lightning
7. Hailstones
8. Thunderstorms
9. Thunderclouds
10. Thunder
11. Lightning
12. Thunder
13. Hailstones
14. Thunderclouds
15. Hailstones
16. Lightning
17. Thunder
18. Thunder
19. Thunderstorms
20. Lightning